The One Story

THE
ONE STORY

By Hulda Niebuhr

ILLUSTRATED BY JOHN LEAR

THE WESTMINSTER PRESS · PHILADELPHIA

PRINTED IN THE UNITED STATES OF AMERICA
AT THE LAKESIDE PRESS
R. R. DONNELLEY & SONS COMPANY, CHICAGO,
AND CRAWFORDSVILLE, INDIANA

CONTENTS

The One Story

PART ONE

I. *PROLOGUE*

THROUGH all the many pages of the Bible runs one great story. That may sound strange to you, who know that the Bible has in it many books and many stories. There are indeed hundreds of stories in the Bible—about good people and bad people, about people who lived in the dim, distant days before history began, and about those who lived less than two thousand years ago. There are many kinds of stories too—history, biography, parable, legend, even a fable or two. There are letters and sermons and songs. Nevertheless, it is true that the Bible is one book that tells one story. The story concerns all the people of the earth, and the chief character in it is the Lord God of heaven and earth.

"In the beginning God created the heaven and the earth"

These are the first words of the Book of Books, and the beginning of the one great story it tells. The Bible does not speak of the millions of years that we know as the ice age and the Stone Age. It does not tell us of an age of trilobites or an age of reptiles.

Scientists learned of these things from fossils and rocks hundreds of years after the first chapter of the Bible was written. The Bible story of the Creation has in it all the grandeur of the story science tells, but its purpose is to answer questions science cannot answer: "Who is back of it all?" "Who planned it all?" It says: "All the world and everything in it is here because God created it. All the beasts and fish and plants, the stars and the sky came into being because God created them. All the beasts and fish and plants, the stars and the sky, came into being because God willed it so."

"God created man in his own image, in the image of God created he him"

Finally God made man, the greatest of his creatures, to rule over the fish of the sea and the birds of the air and the beasts of the field, to have dominion over all the earth. God made man after his own likeness, with a mind able to plan and create and a will free to choose. This man could know God, and, knowing him, could find his only true happiness in fellowship with God, in loving God and doing his will.

God had joy in his creation. When he looked at it all, the ancient story says, "Behold, it was very good." But man, made in God's image, was not content to take the place God had given him in the world. He wanted to be free to go his own way and do as he pleased, apart from God. This led him to disobey God's command.

The sin of man changed the joy of the Creator, God, to sorrow. Man, together with the woman made to be his helpmate, was driven out from the garden God had given him. An angel with a flaming sword guarded it against their return. Their children and their children's children also chose an evil way, and a great flood was sent to punish them. Noah, who was obedient to God, was saved from the flood, together with his family. When it was over, they saw a great rainbow in the clouds and knew it was a sign that God still loved man.

Again and again man rebelled against God. His pride was great, and he thought the way to be truly happy was to do just as he pleased. So God set about winning man to himself. The story of how he did it is the one great story of the Bible.

II. *"I will bless thee, . . . and thou shalt be a blessing"*

WHEN the people of the Bible told the story of their forefather Abraham as it came down to them through the centuries, they began by telling how God spoke to Abraham. They knew God as the living God, who made his will known to the people of earth. What better words could they use than to say, "He spoke," or, "He said," when they wanted to tell that he made his will known to someone?

THERE were many wise and mighty people in the great empires of ancient time, and many who were great and powerful lived in the splendid cities of Egypt and Babylonia. But it was to a simple herdsman that God made his will known when he began to carry out his great plan.

God said to Abraham, who lived in the land of Haran: "Leave this your homeland, and your tribe and your kindred, and go to a land that I will show you. I will make of you a great nation, and through you shall all the nations of the world be blessed."

13

"Leave this land, where my father found pasture for his herd?
Leave my father's family and be a stranger I know not where?"
Abraham knew it was God's command, and he trusted God. So
with his wife Sarah and his nephew Lot, and with his herds of
sheep and cattle in charge of their keepers, Abraham set out to
find a new home. He was guided to the Land of Canaan, a small
country to the west, between Babylonia and Egypt. There he
settled, for he heard the Lord say to him, "To your descendants
will I give this land." The first thing Abraham did in the new
country was to build an altar and worship the Lord.

Among wooded hills, with good lands near for grazing sheep
and cattle, Abraham made his new home. The people who already lived there welcomed him and his household and flocks.
There was plenty of room in the land for newcomers. When he
had pitched his tents in the country where his home would be
Abraham heard God say:

"Look from where you are, to the north and to the south, to
the east and to the west. All the land you see I will give to you and
to your children." But as yet Abraham had no child of his own.
He began to wonder if he had really heard the Lord's promise cor-
rectly. He asked the Lord, "How can you give me this land for
my children and my children's children if I go childless?"

And God answered: "Look toward the heavens and see the
stars. Can you count them? So shall be those that come after you,
countless as the stars." Abraham believed the Lord, and finally,
in his old age, the long-awaited child was born. Abraham and
Sarah named their son Isaac, which means "laughter."

In the land where Abraham lived it was the custom of the people to offer their first-born child as a sacrifice to their gods. When
he thought of this custom, Abraham was deeply troubled. Was
not the Lord God he worshiped as worthy of great gifts as the
gods of his Canaanite neighbors? All that he had was given to him
by God; could he hold back even the greatly loved and long-
promised son? So it came about that Abraham believed that
God's voice said to him, "Take your son, your only son, and offer
him at the sacred place in the land of Moriah."

Sorrowfully, but trusting God completely, Abraham took the
more than three days' journey to the mount of sacrifice, with

Isaac, strong and vigorous, beside him. They carried wood and
fire for the sacrifice. Isaac was puzzled. He said, "My father, we
have fire and wood, but where is the lamb for the sacrifice?"
Abraham answered, "My son, God will provide a lamb for the sacrifice." They came to the sacred place on the mountain, and there
Abraham and Isaac built an altar. When all was prepared for the
sacrifice, and Abraham was ready to offer his son, the true word
of the Lord came to him. It came to him so clearly and surely that
he believed God had sent a messenger to stay his hand, saying,
"Lay not your hand upon the lad!" Abraham turned and saw a
ram caught by his horns in the thicket. He knew then that God
had sent it to him as a sign that he should offer it in place of his
son.

The very hardest thing that could be asked of Abraham—to
give up the son whom he loved—he had been willing to do, trusting that somehow God would keep the promise he had made.
Now he knew that God had taught him a better way to worship.
He returned home with Isaac, certain that God himself had given
his son back to him. And he heard again God's promise: "In your
descendants, who are born of the son I have given you, shall all
the nations of the earth be blessed."

When Isaac grew up he married Rebekah, and had two sons,
Jacob and Esau. When Jacob, the younger son, grew to manhood,
he felt in his heart that the special promise given to Abraham and
Isaac would be fulfilled through him and his children. But Esau,
since he was the elder son, had the right to become the head of the
family. Esau, however, spent most of his time hunting in the
fields. Jacob was sure that he would make a better leader than
Esau. Being still selfish and self-willed, he was determined to get
ahead of Esau and to own his father's herds of goats and sheep. So
when Isaac, now a blind and aged man, prepared to give the blessing that was meant for the new head of the family, Jacob, in his
impatience, cheated and took Esau's place. He had long years in
which to repent, for he had to leave home to escape his brother's
anger and did not dare to return. For a long time he lived in
Haran in the household of his mother's brother Laban, in the
land that had once been the home of his grandfather Abraham.

Jacob loved Laban's daughter Rachel, and her father promised to give her to him as his wife in return for seven years of work. Jacob accepted the terms gladly, and the years seemed short because of his love for Rachel. However, when the time was up, Laban gave him his older daughter, Leah, instead. He said, "It is not done in our country, to give the younger daughter away before the older one, but if you will work for me another seven years, I will give you Rachel also." So Jacob worked for Rachel another seven years, and they seemed short to him for he loved her dearly. After that, he and his family stayed on in Haran for six years. He became the father of a large family and the owner of great flocks and herds. Things did not always go well with him. Often he was homesick, and he had other hardships to bear. When others cheated him, he came to realize how deeply he had wronged his brother, and gradually he became a wiser man. Always he yearned for his homeland until at length he decided to return to Canaan and make peace with the brother he had wronged. But would Esau be willing to make peace?

As Jacob drew near to Canaan, he sent ahead large herds of his caravan as a present to his brother. But he wondered: "Can I do enough to make up to my brother for the wrong I did him? And suppose he makes war on me when I return? Will my family and my herds be safe?" Jacob was so worried that when he came to the Brook Jabbok near his home he stayed up all night praying. There was much fear and selfishness in his heart, yet he was determined to have God's blessing. "I will not let you go," said Jacob to God, "unless you bless me." He felt that he was wrestling with God for a blessing. Finally, at daybreak, when he knew he had God's blessing and had learned to put God's will first, he was such a different man that it seemed he must have a new name. In his prayer he was given the name "Israel," which means "God rules." Because he had received the blessing for which he longed, he named the place "Peniel," or "face of God," for, he said, "Here I have seen God face to face."

When daylight came and Jacob looked into the distance, he saw someone coming, accompanied by four hundred men. Who should it be but his brother Esau! Jacob bowed many times to show that he came in a friendly spirit. He was greatly surprised when Esau ran to meet him and kissed and embraced him. Jacob said, "I have brought these herds as a gift, so that you may be friends with me." Esau answered, "I have enough, my brother; keep what you have." But Jacob insisted, "Rather shall you receive my presents; seeing your face to be friendly is as if I had seen the face of God himself." And again they kissed and embraced each other. So Jacob was happy as he settled in the Land of Canaan, and there his children grew up.

Among Jacob's twelve sons there was one, Joseph, the older of Rachel's two children, whom Jacob loved more than all the others. The others became very jealous of Joseph, and it did not help matters that he grew somewhat vain and boastful. So one day his brothers sold him as a slave to a caravan of merchants going to Egypt. They hoped never to see him again. But first they made Joseph take off the beautiful coat of many colors that Jacob had given him. Then they stained it with goat's blood and showed it to their father, pretending that a wild beast had devoured their brother.

Through much hardship in Egypt, Joseph learned courage and wisdom and trust in God. Because men knew they could trust him, he was given important work to do.

Later Joseph was unjustly charged with wrongdoing and sent to prison. Among the prisoners he became known for his ability to interpret dreams, and that power brought him before Pharaoh, the ruler of Egypt. Pharaoh wanted to know the meaning of certain dreams that none of the Egyptian interpreters could explain.

"God sent those dreams," Joseph said, "to tell Pharaoh that a long time of famine is coming, and to show what must be done to prepare so that the people will not starve." The plans Joseph suggested were so wise that Pharaoh said, "Since your God has told you all these things, none other will be so well fitted to carry out these plans." And he made Joseph governor of the country and keeper of all the granaries.

Years of famine came to Egypt and to all the neighboring lands, including Canaan. In Egypt alone was there a store of grain. When Jacob sent his sons there to buy food, could they have guessed they would see their brother, sold long years ago into slavery? It did not enter their minds that the governor of the granaries, in his beautiful clothes and his Egyptian headdress, could be anyone they had ever seen before. But Joseph recognized his brothers. As soon as he saw them, he yearned to be friends with them and to see his father again.

He observed them carefully without their realizing it and learned that now they had become kinder, that they protected Benjamin, the youngest in the family, and that the sorrow of their father over the loss of Joseph had gone to their hearts. At last he made himself known to them, saying: "I am Joseph. Does my father still live?" They were so frightened that they could not answer. Joseph comforted them, saying: "Do not grieve because you sold me into Egypt. God sent me before you that you might live and not perish." Then he sent for all the family to come and live in Egypt, where he could look after them. Pharaoh received most graciously the old father, Jacob, now known as Israel, and honored him. He also gave him a home in the land of Goshen, which is a district in the northeast of the great land of Egypt.

The "children of Israel" stayed on in Egypt; and after them their children's children, who came to be known as Israelites, grew up in that country. Not all of them remembered God's promise to their forefather Abraham, but there were some among them who never forgot it. Although they had never seen the Land of Canaan, they knew it to be their true home, where they would one day live as God's own people. They saw that the Egyptians lived in fear of their many gods, but the Israelites knew that they could trust their God, the God of Abraham and Isaac and Jacob. Had he not promised that he would keep them in his care?

III. *"Thus saith the Lord . . . , O Israel, Fear not: for I have redeemed thee, I have called thee by thy name; thou art mine"*

THIS is a story full of "signs and wonders and mighty works." Exactly what happened is not always entirely clear from the ancient records, but the fact *is* clear that God used his power to deliver his chosen people from slavery.

L IFE was very different in the land of Goshen at the time when Moses was born—very different indeed from the days when the children of Israel were befriended by Pharaoh. Joseph and his father were forgotten, and the new ruler thought about the Israelites only because he needed slave labor. The overseers with their whips were always behind them while they worked from early morning until late at night. The Egyptian sun was very hot, but often slaves had to work in it until they were overcome by the heat. Many Israelites died of exhaustion while making the bricks needed for the building of the great treasure cities that Pharaoh had planned. They helped to erect palaces and enormous storehouses and temples and huge fortifications. Those who cultivated the land were at the mercy of their masters too, with no rights and no liberty. There was no one in the government to whom they could appeal, no one who cared whether or not they were treated justly.

There came a still harder time when Pharaoh feared for his kingdom. He remembered an invasion of earlier times and thought: "If there should be an invasion or a rebellion again, these Hebrews, these foreigners on the border of our country, will join with the enemy and undo us. We must not let them grow in numbers." Therefore he gave command that all Israelite boy babies be thrown into the River Nile.

During these days the child Moses was born. His mother hid him in a basket boat at the spot where Pharaoh's daughter went bathing, and there the princess found the baby in the bulrushes. "It is one of the Hebrew children," she said, and decided to adopt the baby and keep him safe. His sister, Miriam, had been keeping watch over him. When she heard the princess she ran to her at once and asked, "Shall I call one of the Hebrew women to nurse the baby for you?" The princess, glad for the suggestion, said, "Yes, do!" and Miriam ran to get her mother. So it came about that Moses' own mother could bring him up under the protection of the princess.

It was quite wonderful that he could grow up at the Egyptian royal court and also under his mother's care. If he had lived as a slave child, he would have had no schooling. He would have been sent, when just a small boy, to do slave labor in the fields. Instead, he was taught all the wisdom of the Egyptians. He studied with the best teachers of the time, for Egyptian scholars were known for their learning in law, in astronomy, and in many other subjects. But Moses' mother did not let him forget his Israelite birth. She taught him to be proud of his forefathers—Abraham, Isaac, and Jacob. She told him of God's promises to them, of their faith in God, of their obedience to him, and of the hope of the people of Israel for the Promised Land.

One day when Moses had grown to manhood, he saw an Egyptian striking a slave, one of his own Israelite people. In great anger Moses killed the Egyptian. Later, when he found that his deed had become known, he fled from the country. For many years he lived in the desert of Midian, far to the east, herding sheep. There he had time to think of his hasty deed, of the sorrows of his people, and of God's promises to his forefather Abraham. There Moses prayed for his people that they might be delivered from slavery.

One day Moses herded his flock near the foot of Mount Sinai. He was thinking of his people, who, even though God had promised them a great future, seemed now to be doomed to perish. Then he had a vision. He saw a bush on the hillside that was on fire, yet was not burning up. "God is telling me," he thought. "that my people will not perish in their troubles." He took off his shoes in reverence, and he heard God speak to him out of the flaming bush: "I am the God of your fathers, the God of Abraham and Isaac and Jacob. You will know who I am from the things that will happen and from the way in which I will lead you. The prayers of the children of Israel have come to me, and I have seen how the Egyptians oppress them. Come now, I will send you to Pharaoh that you may bring forth my people, the children of Israel, out of Egypt."

Moses had been praying that someone might arise to free his people from slavery. But when he was called to do this task himself, he objected. "Who am I to do this hard thing?" he asked. And the Lord answered: "You will not be doing this in your own strength. I will be with you. This will be proof to you that I am sending you: you will worship me here at this mountain with the children of Israel, a free people."

"Suppose they do not believe that you have appeared to me?" he said to the Lord. "Suppose they do not believe that I was sent to them?"

Then God said: "Who has made man's mouth? Have not I, the Lord? I will teach you what you must say when the time comes." And Moses was encouraged by these words.

There was another big question. Would Pharaoh let the people leave the country? They were his slaves. They did much work for him. Why should he let them go?

"When I have done what I shall do," the Lord promised Moses, "then Pharaoh will let them go."

Now Moses knew what he must do. With his brother, Aaron, beside him, he told the people of Israel about the Lord's promises. When the people realized that they had not been forgotten, when they heard the plans for deliverance from bondage, they bowed their heads and worshiped the Lord.

Pharaoh, however, would not listen to Moses and Aaron. He was more interested in keeping his slave labor than in hearing the word of the Hebrews' God. When Moses and Aaron appeared before him, saying, "The Lord God of Israel says, Let my people go," he answered, "Who is the Lord, that I should obey his voice to let Israel go?"

Then great trouble came to the land of Egypt. There were swarms of locusts and storms of hail to ruin the crops. There were plagues that sickened the people, and fearful darkness to cover the land. The Nile River, on which they depended for irrigation, was polluted. One plague followed hard upon the other.

In the course of each plague, Moses and his brother appeared before Pharaoh to bring the word, "Thus says the Lord, Let my people go, that they may serve me." Each time Pharaoh promised, "When the suffering from this plague is ended, I will let them go." Each time, as soon as God removed the plague and the Israelites were about to go, Pharaoh hardened his heart and would not let the people go. Rather than free them, he made their tasks harder. They were beaten when they could not do the impossible. Their suffering caused even Moses to lose faith for a time. Then once more he heard the Lord's promise to the people: "I will keep you. You shall be my people, and you shall know that I am your God. I will bring you to the land I promised Abraham, for I am the Lord." Moses again believed, but because of their bitter hardship the people would not listen to him.

Then a plague came that brought death even into Pharaoh's own family. Pharaoh did not wait for Moses and Aaron to come bidding him in God's name, "Let my people go!" He called them to him in the night and said: "Rise up, and go from among my people, both you and the children of Israel. Go, serve God, as you have said."

With joy in their hearts the people fled from Rameses, the beautiful city they had worked as slaves to build. They did not travel the great military road that led straight to the Land of Canaan. Instead, they started for the wilderness east of the Red Sea, where God had directed Moses to bring them. They took with them all their belongings—flocks and herds, household goods, gold and jewels. They carried dough for unleavened bread, and in the morning they made fires and baked cakes of it for breakfast.

Suddenly word came that Pharaoh was breaking his word by sending his soldiers and chariots after them. The Israelites were caught between a sea on the border of Egypt and the chariots of the Egyptians. They cried to Moses, "Were there no graves in Egypt that we must die in the wilderness?" But Moses heard the Lord say, "Tell the children of Israel to go forward."

As they hurried along they knew that the Egyptian chariots were always back of them. Whatever would they do when they came to the edge of the sea? But when they came to the sea—they found a way made for them to the other side. A strong wind drove back the waters, and the Israelites found a marshy place where they could cross on foot. But the chariots of the Egyptians could not cross. When they tried to do so, they were caught in the midst of the returning waters and drowned. The Israelites knew that God had delivered them in a time of great danger. When a new day dawned, the people were safe on the other side, and their enemies were destroyed. Moses' sister, Miriam, took a timbrel in her hand, and all the women brought their timbrels and danced for joy.

They all rejoiced greatly, but it was Moses who realized how truly great was their deliverance. He told them: "It was the Lord who redeemed you. How else could a forlorn slave people be freed from the mighty Egyptian empire? He has you on his heart and mind." And he led the people in a song of thanksgiving: "The Lord is my strength and song, and he is become my salvation!"

The children of Israel now had new faith in God and in his servant Moses. But as the days of travel through the wilderness went on, they often complained of their hardships. In their long years as slaves, every day had been like another. Now when troubles came that they had not foreseen, they became so frightened that they forgot their faith in God. Later when Moses looked back and remembered how little faith the people had, he understood why the Lord guided him to take a very roundabout way to the Promised Land. They needed time to learn many things before they could be a nation that trusted God. As he had promised Moses, God cared for their wants. Flocks of quail, resting in the desert on their flight, supplied meat. Often in the morning the people found on the ground an excitingly sweet food that tasted like wafers made of honey. They called this food "manna." It melted in the sun, and had to be eaten on the day it was gathered. That they might have water to drink, Moses, who knew the desert so well, found places among the rocks where springs flowed.

There were still dangers to be faced, but at least the people were safely out of Egypt and on their way to the mountain where the Lord had promised Moses they would worship him.

IV. *"If ye will obey my voice ...,*
and keep my covenant, then ye shall be
a peculiar treasure unto me above all people:
for all the earth is mine"

IN THE Bible we read of various ways in which God made his will known to people, always speaking to them in a manner they could understand. The children of Israel thought of fire as a sign of God's presence. Thunder and lightning made him seem very near. But it was as Moses waited alone in prayer before God on the mountainside that he learned the things Israel needed most to know.

The people were used to a ceremony known as the "rite of the covenant," when a promise was made that would be binding always. Therefore the fact that God made a covenant with them had great meaning for them.

MILE after mile, the children of Israel journeyed through the desert toward the sacred mountain where God had promised he would meet them. There were no mountains in

25

sight now. The road lead over dry, sandy stretches and over stony
tableland. Now and then, there would be springs of water with
palm trees beside them giving shade from the bright sun. When
the people came to such a spot, they forgot for a time their sufferings from thirst or hunger and they rested at ease.

One day there was a pleasant excitement among them, for they
were approaching such an oasis. Moses told them about its many
trees and the sparkling stream that ran through a valley between
rocky cliffs. When they came to the valley, it was as green and
restful as they had hoped. Great was their relief, after the long,
dusty road, when they drank the clear water of the stream and
pitched their tents beside it for a rest. But things did not always
go so well with them.

At Rephidim there was trouble with one of the rough desert
tribes who feared the Israelites might want to take possession of
their territory. When the enemy attacked them, Moses said to
his chief assistant, Joshua, "Take our strong young men and defend our camp, and I will go on the hill with the rod of God in my
hand." The people had seen that staff in Moses' hand as he led
them through all the hardships of their journey and he had used it
to open springs of water in the rocks. Therefore they had come to
believe that God worked through it in a special way. Perhaps
Moses thought so too, for he held it high as he stood on the hill
overlooking the battleground.

Joshua and the young men fought successfully until Moses became too weary to stand holding his arms so high; then the enemy
were able to push them back. "Our men must not think you have
given up," said Moses' brother, Aaron. So he found a stone for
Moses to sit on while he and his friend Hur stood on either side of
Moses, supporting his arms as he held them high. They kept his
hands steady until sundown, when the enemy were routed.

When the people had rested at Rephidim for a time, they
started on their journey again and came to the desert of Midian.
They pitched their tents where Moses had herded sheep so many
years while he was in exile from Egypt. They stayed here for
quite a while because Moses needed time to set many things in
order. He worked from morning until evening helping the people settle all sorts of quarrels and misunderstandings, applying

the laws that all of them had known for years. But also he kept
trying to understand better what God's will was for his people.

It was too much for one man to judge all Israel, and so here in
Midian Moses established a system of government. He chose able
men from among the people and put them as elders over tens and
over fifties and hundreds and a thousand, and they served as
judges over the people at all times. They could bring the hard
cases to Moses, but all small matters they judged themselves according to instruction in the law that Moses gave them.

When the people had rested in Midian, they traveled on. Being
used to the flat Egyptian river land, they could hardly believe
their eyes when they reached the huge granite mountains in the
desert country. They were filled with wonder at the sight of the
gleaming colors, the bright sun making still brighter the deep
streaks of red and purple and green in the gray and brown of the
vast piles of stone that seemed to rise to the sky. They pitched
camp at the foot of the highest mountain, the one they had
thought about through all their journey. Moses had told them
God's promise: "At this mountain I will meet them, a free people, for I am the Lord."

With the help of the elders, Moses made preparation for the
people to celebrate their thanksgiving and to take on the duties
their deliverance had brought them. Bounds were put around
the mountain so that no one might climb it or even touch it.
Moses asked the people to prepare their hearts and minds and to
wash their clothes, for they were to appear before the Lord. On
the third day, there came thunder and lightning, and the whole
mountain began to quake and to smoke. Moses asked the people
to come forth from their tents and assemble, but they were frightened and stood far off. Between thunder and lightning they saw a
fiery cloud covering the top of the mountain and they said to
Moses, "Speak you with us, and we will hear: but do not let God
speak with us, or we will die."

Moses went up the mountain and stayed a long time. When he
came down he was carrying some tablets of stone with the laws of
God carved upon them. As he came near the camp, he saw the
people singing and dancing around an idol that was in the form
of a golden calf. In his horror he smashed the tablets of the law

upon the rocks, and, calling Aaron to him, he reproached him.

"How could you let this happen and bring such great sin upon our people?" he demanded of him.

Aaron answered: "You were away so long that the people did not know what had become of you. They asked me to make a god for them, and when I melted their earrings and other jewelry there came out this calf."

Moses feared that for this terrible sin God would cast his people off completely. He prayed to God for them: "O God, these my people have sinned a great sin. Forgive them, if you can. If not, then blot my name out of the book of life."

As Moses prayed, assurance came to him that God's purpose for his people could not fail. They would suffer greatly for their sin, but they would be led forward to a new understanding of his ways with them. Again Moses brought to the people tablets of stone with the words of the law written on them. As he came to them, his face shone, and they could see he had been with God.

"You shall never make gods of silver or of gold," he warned them, "for our God is the Lord who talked with us from heaven, and this is his message: 'I am the Lord your God, who brought you out of the land of Egypt, out of the house of bondage. You shall have no other gods before me.' "

Then Moses told them the other laws they must obey: God commanded them to keep his name and day holy, to honor their parents, neither to kill nor to steal nor to commit adultery, not to speak untruthfully of one another, nor to covet what belonged to others. "All this he expects of us if we are to be his people," he said.

Moses told them again: "It was only because the Lord God was with us that we are here. It was he who led us out of Egypt and redeemed us from slavery. He caused winds and plagues and clouds and thunders to happen, and quails and manna to come, and water springs to open for our thirst. All this he did, not because we are a people better than others, but because he has a plan for us. He has chosen us. 'If you will obey my voice,' says the Lord, 'and keep my covenant, you shall be a peculiar treasure to me above all people, for all the earth is mine.' "

The people answered as with one voice: "All the words that

the Lord has said we will do. We will keep his law and do his will. The Lord only shall be our God."

So it was that God made a covenant with the people of Israel, through the fire and the thunder and the earthquake, and through the word that Moses brought to them from God. No matter what gods other peoples might worship, they knew that the Lord who had redeemed them was their God who ruled over them and whose will they must obey.

To help them with their worship Moses directed the people in making a chest of acacia wood, known as the Ark. Into it were put the tablets of stone he had brought from the mountain. It was carried before them in their journeys from that time on, to remind them that the Lord did not dwell in any one spot. Although he had met them on the mountain, he did not live just there, but he was with them always. Moses told them that the Lord had said, "I will walk among you." The tablets of stone reminded them that they had promised to obey the laws of the Lord.

The people made a Tabernacle, a sacred tent, woven of goat's hair and furnished as beautifully as desert life made possible. Whenever they rested from their journeying, they would set it up and put the Ark into the part of it known as the "Holy of Holies." They believed that the glory of the Lord was there in a very special way. Before the Tabernacle they would set up an altar for burnt offerings. Some priests were appointed to lead the worship. Aaron, the brother of Moses, was made chief priest.

The Israelites had become a nation, dedicated to the service of the Lord God. They had a government, and a place and manner of worship. But they were not yet ready to enter the Promised Land. During the stretch of journey that was left, they were often fainthearted and even rebellious over the hardships of the desert, which they called "the great and terrible wilderness." It was indeed a very hard journey, but there was never more trouble than they could bear. Always there was help. Moses, to whom the ways of the Lord were so clear, prayed that God would forgive them for their disobedience and lack of faith.

At last, the Israelites came near the promised Land of Canaan. Moses sent out spies to investigate the land and to bring back reports about it. Was it fruitful? Were there few or many people? Were they strong or weak? Did they live in cities or in tents, or perhaps even in fortresses? The spies came back with contradictory reports. Some of them could see only trouble ahead. "The cities have strong walls around them, and great giants live in them." These worried men said, "We seemed to ourselves like grasshoppers beside them."

Joshua, and Caleb, who had been with him, reported otherwise. They had seen what the others learned in time to be the truth. "The people of the land have no spirit," Joshua said, "no courage. They are not united. There is no real strength in them. The Lord is with us, so have no fear of them." But a great many people did not believe Joshua and Caleb.

Brought up in Egypt as slaves, many of the Israelites did not have enough courage to go up against a country that had walled fortresses in it. Therefore, plans had to be changed. The people had to stay in the wilderness for many long years, until a hardier race grew up, taught by Moses and Joshua and by others of the older people whose faith was strong.

When at last the Israelites reached Moab and were ready to enter Canaan, Moses was an aged man. He climbed to the top of Mount Nebo, where he could see the land that had been in his mind and hopes for so many years. He never came down from the mountain. When the people had watched for him a long time in vain, they knew that he had died there. They taught their children that the Lord himself showed Moses the Promised Land, from the north to the south and from the eastern desert to the sea, and that when Moses died, the Lord himself laid his body to rest in a grave no man had ever seen. They mourned for him and knew that there was no one like him of whom they could say, "He knew the Lord face to face."

Moses had appointed Joshua his successor, and because the people trusted Moses and because Joshua had proved himself a wise leader, they were glad to follow him. Now it was Joshua's task to lead them into the Promised Land.

V. *"Thou shalt have no other gods before me"*

THE story of the conquest of the Promised Land, as we have it in the Bible, has been woven together by the Bible writers out of two stories from different sets of inherited memories. One story says that Joshua and his troops conquered the country quickly, after the miraculous fall of the walls of Jericho. The other story tells how the country was conquered "by little and little," and how in the process the people learned to distinguish their God from the gods of the heathen. The first expresses above all the wonder of the people at God's guidance and help; the second gives a clearer picture of the historical events.

IT SEEMED a great and fearful task—to lead the children of Israel into a land occupied by other peoples. But the Lord encouraged Joshua: "Be strong and of good courage; be not afraid. As I was with Moses, so I will be with you. I will not fail you, nor forsake you."

Spies whom Joshua had sent ahead to the city of Jericho came back saying: 'The people of Jericho have heard how our God led us with a mighty hand out of Egypt. They are afraid of us; terror has fallen upon them."

The gates of the city had been locked because a siege was ex
pected; but no one expected the strange sort of siege that Joshua
directed at the Lord's command. As the guards of the walls of
Jericho looked down and watched the Israelite hosts, their terror
must have increased, for what they saw day after day was weirdly
different from all other sieges they had ever heard about.

Early in the morning, each morning for six days, they saw a
religious procession, rather than a march of warriors, encircling
their city. Seven priests blowing rams'-horn trumpets led the
march. Then came the army, then those carrying the Ark of the
Covenant. The rest of the people followed, and none of them ut-
tered a sound. Except for the priests' trumpets they marched in
complete silence, for Joshua had told them, "No, sound shall
come from your mouths until I bid you to shout!" When they
had circled the city, they all retired to their camp. The people of
Jericho must have wondered what would happen next.

On the seventh day the Israelites rose at dawn to circle the city
and this time they went around seven times silently. At the
seventh time Joshua commanded, "Shout, for the Lord has given
you the city!"

When the ruins of ancient Jericho were dug out in our time,
the walls were found toppled over as if an earthquake had oc-
curred. The wonder was that by God's providence it happened
when Israel was entering the Promised Land. The ancient story
says, "They shouted with a great shout," and as the people
shouted, the walls of the city fell. The Israelites walked in and
took the city. In those days taking a city meant destroying it, and
the word of the destruction of Jericho brought terror to all the
country round about.

Joshua's armed men pushed forward into the country. When
they had conquered several towns and had camped at Gilgal,
there arrived a deputation of men in ragged clothes, with worn-
out shoes upon their feet and mended wineskins upon their don-
keys' backs. They said: "We have come from a far country. We
have heard the fame of your God, and all he did for you in Egypt
and as you came to this country. Therefore the elders of our
country sent us to make a treaty of peace with you. We want to be
your servants."

They took bread out of their sacks and it appeared dry and moldy. They said: "This bread we took hot out of our ovens when we left our country, and our wineskins were new. Our shoes are worn and our garments torn from our long travel to see you." Joshua made a treaty with them and they left to return to their homes. How embarrassed he was when, a little farther on, his army came upon these same people in Gibeon! They were in reality citizens of a neighboring city, fearing destruction by the Israelites. Many of Joshua's soldiers wanted to destroy the city anyway, but the leaders said: "We may not touch them because of the promise we made before the Lord God of Israel. But they said they would be our servants, and so they shall be." The Gibeonites were spared, but they and their descendants had to carry water and cut wood for the Israelites.

There were some very strong walled fortresses in the land, but Joshua did not lead the people to those strongly fortified sections of the country. They went rather into the hill country, where the Canaanites were not strong and where the Israelites in some places found tribes that knew of the God of Abraham and Isaac and Jacob. With these people they made friendly treaties.

When the people asked, "How is it that so many Canaanite cities are not as strong as their walls made you think?" Joshua could answer: "It is as I told you long ago when I spied out the country for Moses; there is no spirit in the people. No man trusts any other; they are not united. Many of them, you can see, are slaves to the few wealthy ones who own chariots and big houses. Slaves do not care who owns the land. And they all worship gods that have no power!"

There were large sections of the country that Joshua and his army could not conquer, but they did have many victories. The people of Israel soon were fairly well established in many parts of Canaan. At last there came more peaceful times. Then Joshua called all the leaders of the tribes together and divided the land. Most of the southern section was given to the descendants of Jacob's sons Judah and Simeon. Benjamin, the smallest of the tribes, was assigned to a section of the hill country next to Judah. Joseph's descendants, the tribes of Ephraim and Manasseh, settled in the country north of that; and all the other tribes settled beyond, to the north and the east. Each Israelite was to have his own piece of land, and none was to be slave to another.

Across the country and along the coast there were a number of strong Canaanite cities. The Israelites and Canaanites lived as neighbors and married into each other's families or tribes.

Joshua saw this as a great danger. The Canaanites were a clever people and could build good houses and grow fine crops. The people of Israel, tired of the desert life, envied the Canaanites their festivals, in which they sang songs and played musical instruments, making much better music than the Israelites had ever heard before. The Canaanites were good at writing too. They used an alphabet they themselves had invented. But the Canaanites worshiped many gods, and Israel had promised to serve the one Lord God, who had chosen them for his people. Joshua feared that the people, while learning good things from the Canaanites, might lose their greatest possession, their faith in the Lord God who had made a covenant with them. Joshua and the thoughtful elders who helped him lead the people were troubled when on every hill, under every ancient tree, beside the wells and springs, they noticed stones and poles representing Canaanite gods, and altars on which the Canaanites made sacrifices to their chief gods, Baal and Astarte. They heard the Canaanite people tell stories of whole families of gods. The festivals held to honor these gods included wicked practices, which were revolting to Joshua and to the other leaders.

They asked one another: "As our people learn to tend vines and to raise flocks, will they believe what the Canaanites say, that nothing will grow unless their gods are worshiped and that it is the gods who make the land fertile?" Or the children of Israel might think that Baal was their own God with a different name, and worship him in the unholy way of the Canaanites. It might be that they would be influenced by the clans descended from Abraham that did not go to Egypt. These groups did not know God's covenant with Israel and did not know the laws of Moses. Suppose Israel should forget the covenant and no longer keep the Lord's commandments?

Joshua was quite an old man by now and he wanted to make good use of the time that was left to him. So he called a great

meeting of all the people and he said to them: "I have lived long
and shall soon die. In your hearts you know that there is not
one promise the Lord has made that he has failed to keep. It is
not through our might or our power or our wisdom that we have
this land, but through the mighty acts of the Lord God who has
made us his people. If you do not serve the Lord as you have
promised, if you serve strange gods instead, then you will perish
from this land."

The people said to one another, "God forbid that we should
forsake the Lord and serve other gods." As Joshua went on, they
felt how strong was his faith and how deep his concern for them:
"It may be that you will decide not to serve the Lord. Choose
you today whom you will serve. As for me and my house, we will
serve the Lord." The people answered with one voice, "We too
will serve the Lord and his voice we will obey."

Then Joshua set up a great stone under a terebinth tree beside the Tabernacle, to remind the people that they owed obedience to God.

But in the years to come they did not always remember. Punishment came quickly, for when they left the worship of the
Lord God and followed the ways of the Canaanites, they were no
longer a united people and they began to quarrel with one another. Then the enemy tribes in and around the land were able
to overcome them. Their leaders during these years were known
as judges. Again and again there arose to deliver them a judge
whom God had chosen. The people could see that his actions
were divinely guided.

Once the Canaanites under Sisera came against them in the
great Valley of Esdraelon with nine hundred iron chariots. The
Israelites had no chariots at all. It looked as if everything were
lost, but Deborah the prophetess knew otherwise. She lived
under a certain palm tree, where the children of Israel came to
her for advice and judgment. In the name of the Lord she sent
a message to Barak, another leader of the people, to ask that he
muster an army. "The Lord has promised," she said, "that he
will deliver Sisera into your hand." "I will go if you will go with
Me," Barak replied. So Deborah went with him, and between
them they stirred up the courage of the tribes to go against the

great army. During the battle a mighty storm arose. The rain poured down, making mud of the great open valley so that the iron chariots became a hindrance, and the enemy was routed. The children of Israel celebrated the victory in a song: "Some trust in chariots and some in horses, but we will remember the name of the Lord our God." Deborah sang, "The stars in their courses fought against Sisera!"

After a time, the people again left the worship of the Lord and sacrificed to Baal in great numbers. Then another enemy tribe, the Midianites, overran the country. There seemed to be no hope of standing against them. But the word of the Lord came to a young man named Gideon, telling him to destroy the altar that his father had built to Baal and to build instead one to the Lord God of Israel. The Lord said to him, "You shall save Israel from the Midianites, for I have sent you." Gideon was doubtful at first, but when he was persuaded that the Lord was indeed with him and had chosen him, he sent messengers to the tribes with a command that they arise and join him in driving out the invaders. They came from east and west and north and south, thirty-two thousand in all. As they gathered about Gideon, they saw the enemy's black tents covering the valley like a swarm of locusts and it seemed to them that the Midianites' camels were as many as the sands of the sea.

Gideon knew there was something else more important than numbers, so he gave a very unexpected order: "Whoever is fearful and afraid, let him leave Mount Gilead and return home." When all had left who were glad to go, there remained only ten thousand men. But Gideon knew that not all of these ten thousand could be depended on in battle. So he led them on a march past a brook and watched them as they took a drink. Most of them knelt down by the brook and enjoyed the water, but three hundred drank out of their hands, bending over but remaining alert, in the manner of good soldiers. He sent the rest home and told the three hundred, "The Lord has revealed to me that he has delivered the Midianite army into our hands."

To his army of three hundred he gave strange equipment and strange orders: He divided them into three groups of a hundred each to come quietly upon the Midianite army from three sides, each man carrying in his right hand a trumpet, in his left a jug concealing a torch. They were to get close to the Midianite camp, wait for his signal, and do as he did. At his signal each blew his trumpet and shouted, "The sword of the Lord, and of Gideon." Then they broke their pitchers, exposing the lights, and rushed to the attack. The Midianites, suddenly wakened from sleep, heard the trumpets and the battle cry and saw the flickering lights close upon them. In the confusion and darkness they could not distinguish enemy from comrade, and so destroyed one another. So great was their fear that shortly they fled in panic, Gideon and his men pursuing them.

Gideon proved a strong leader. The Israelites wanted to make him their king, but he said, "I will not be king, for the Lord is ruler over you."

There was peace for a while, but after Gideon's death a new enemy appeared. The Israelites had grown weak and were no longer united. The Philistines, a warlike people who had settled on the coast and built strong fortresses there, took advantage of their weakness. The Israelites lost battle after battle against them. Finally, in desperation, they decided to take the Ark of the Covenant into battle, believing that then the Lord's presence would surely be with them. But the Philistines routed them, captured the Ark, and took it to their camp. The people of Israel did not know where to turn. They thought the Lord had forsaken them and they were utterly discouraged.

At the time there was one leader among the people of Israel whom they trusted as a man of God. They knew that since the days of his childhood God's voice had come to Samuel and that he listened. Samuel said to them, "If you return to the Lord with all your hearts and put away the idols you have been worshiping, if you serve the Lord only, he will deliver you from the Philistines." They obeyed, and followed Samuel and the others who had held fast to their covenant with the Lord God. With Samuel to lead them, a new spirit came upon the people, and when the Philistines attacked them again, the Israelites won the battle. Samuel set up a memorial stone and called it "Ebenezer," meaning "stone of help." "This stone shall be witness," he told the people, "that the Lord has helped us."

The Philistines returned the Ark after a time, but the people of Israel had begun to learn that the Lord's presence was not in the Ark. Had he not been with them in the wilderness before they had the Ark? Samuel helped them see that their God was great above all the gods of Canaan. The Promised Land was the Lord's land, all of it; his was the power in it. The people began to ask whether the Canaanite gods were really gods at all. Perhaps they did not really count. Probably they did have some power, the children of Israel thought. But whether they had any power or not, the Israelites knew they had promised to serve the Lord God and him only, whatever other gods there might be. For a while Samuel helped them keep their covenant, but it was not easy. The Canaanite gods promised so much and expected so little.

Their enemies, especially the Philistines, kept on plaguing them. At last the people of Israel decided that they wanted a king. The other nations around them had kings to unite them and lead them. Why should they not have a king to help them out of their troubles?

VI. *"The Lord reigneth . . . . Thy throne is established of old"*

GOD was Israel's King and Lord, to whom the nation owed obedience. When God made his covenant with the people they had promised to live under his rule. At first, the leaders interpreted this to mean that Israel might have no earthly ruler. But when conditions made government by a king necessary, it was understood that he ruled as God's own representative, God's "anointed one," and that he was responsible to God for his actions. Often the kings forgot this and thought only of their own power. Although he had great faults, David reigned with the intention of serving the Lord. For that reason, and also because he lifted Israel as a nation to a new freedom and prosperity, he was remembered by the people as the best of all their kings. They idealized him, and in their later, less happy, years, when they dreamed of a better future, they felt sure God would send them a son of David to rule them.

SAMUEL was troubled. Clearly the people of Israel needed strong leadership to unite them and to overthrow the Philistine control of their country. They said they wanted a king. They

insisted upon a king! And they were trusting Samuel to find the
right man for them. "Give us a king," they had said to Samuel,
"that he may judge us, since you are old now, and that he may
lead us in battle as the kings of the other nations do."

Samuel saw their point. But he knew also that they ought not
to be like other nations. In the wilderness they had entered into a
covenant that the Lord God should rule over them. God was
their king, and they had promised to obey his will.

He prayed to God about it, and a clear answer came to him.
"Give them a king," the Lord said. And there were directions to
guide Samuel: "Tomorrow there will come to you a man from
the tribe of Benjamin whom you shall anoint king over my
people."

On the next day there came from the land of Benjamin a man
looking for some strayed asses of his father's. His name was Saul,
and he was known to be a head taller than anyone else in the
land, a man of kingly appearance and good sense, who served the
Lord God, and whom the people trusted. It was best for the king
to be from Benjamin, the smallest of the tribes. If he were chosen
from one of the larger and stronger tribes, there would be jeal-
ousy among the others. Samuel knew that Saul was the man
whom the Lord had chosen to rule over the people.

Samuel invited Saul into his home and they talked together.
When Samuel found that Saul also had the troubles of the people
on his heart, he was relieved and happy. He provided for a sacrificial meal at the sacred high place, and gave Saul the place of
honor among the thirty present. Afterward Samuel took Saul
with him to sit on the roof of his house and they talked together,
until late in the evening, about the people of Israel and their
future, and how they might be aroused to unite and to overthrow
the oppressor. "And the man who rules over them," Samuel said
"must always remember that he represents the Lord God, for
the Lord God is their king."

Saul knew the people wanted a king. Could Samuel have him
in mind? It looked so, but how could it be?

When Saul rose early the next morning, Samuel walked with
him to the edge of the town. At parting, he said to him, "Stand
still, and I will show you what is God's word for you." He took a

vial of oil and poured it on Saul's head as a sign of kingship, kissed him, and said: "The Lord has anointed you to be king over his people. The Spirit of the Lord will come upon you so that he may rule his people through you." When Saul turned from Samuel, he found that God was giving him new understanding and courage so that he put his gift for leading people at the Lord's service. Samuel asked him to say nothing of the anointing for the present, and Saul went straight home, for Samuel assured him that the lost asses had been found.

One evening soon after this, Saul's anger and pity were aroused. "The people of Jabesh-gilead are desperate," was the news. "The Ammonites are encamped around the city and threaten to destroy them." Saul immediately sent messengers all over the land, asking that the men of Israel gather to free the people of Jabesh. He threatened to punish any who would not come. "Here is a leader among us!" they said as they came in great numbers. With Saul in command, they freed the city in just one day. They said, "Here is a leader indeed."

Samuel called a meeting at the sacred place in Gilgal and said to the people, "Do you see whom the Lord has chosen, that there is none like him among the people?" and they all shouted, "God save the king!" Then Samuel brought a thank offering to the Lord and proclaimed Saul king, saying: "Behold the king you wanted. The Lord has set him over you. Remember all that the Lord has done for you and serve him with all your heart, both you and the king. I will not cease to pray for you and will teach you the good and right way, for if you do wicked things you will be consumed, both you and your king."

For a number of years Saul reigned well. He judged the people, and he kept the Philistines in check with the help of his courageous son Jonathan. But then Saul's pride and sense of power grew so great that he began to make decisions and give commands which he himself knew were against God's will. At war with himself, he became melancholy over his own highhanded actions, so that his servants were deeply troubled about his black moods. Samuel grieved over him, and prayed for him all night long. After a time, however, he saw that the Lord's Spirit had left Saul, and that the Lord had rejected him as king. Samuel was not willing any longer to be an adviser to Saul and retired to his old home in Ramah.

The king had several very devoted servants. They noticed that music soothed his distracted mind, so they persuaded him to send for David, a young shepherd lad from Bethlehem who was known for the songs he sang to the music of his harp. "He is pleasant and wise," they said, "and he is a valiant young man besides being a good musician." Saul loved David and made him his armor-bearer. Whenever he was heavy in spirit, David would play to him on his harp and Saul's heart would grow lighter. David made many friends at Saul's court, but Jonathan, Saul's son, became his closest friend, and remained his friend even when David became so popular and so much of a leader that the prince might have been envious.

It was different with King Saul. When he noticed how the people made a hero of David, his mind became even more troubled. He still loved David, but at the same time he began to grow very jealous of him. At last Jonathan had to warn David that his life was in danger. David fled, and many discontented men from all over Israel joined him.

Saul now feared David as a rival to his throne. He became so obsessed with fear that he spent much of his time pursuing David through the hills and caves and woods. One time, when Saul was camping for the night with his spear stuck in the ground at his head and all his guards sleeping about him, David came upon him. Abishai, who was with David, said: "Let me kill him with this spear. The Lord has put him into your hands." But David forbade Abishai to touch him. "It would be guilt against the Lord himself," he said, "to touch the Lord's anointed!" He took Saul's spear and stole away unnoticed. When they had come to a far hill, David called to Saul's general: "See the king's spear! Let one of the young men come and fetch it." Saul heard, and he called, "Is that your voice, my son David?" David answered, "It is my voice, my lord king!" Then Saul begged David to return home. "I will not do you any more harm," he said, "for I see that my life was precious in your sight." Then Saul abandoned his pursuit, but he and David did not trust each other, and David stayed on the outskirts of Israel, under Philistine protection.

Finally there came a great battle with the Philistines in which Saul and three of his sons, including Jonathan, were killed. David was free then to return home, but he was also sad. He sang a song of lament over them: "Daughters of Israel, weep over Saul. I am distressed for you, my brother Jonathan. How are the mighty fallen!" David settled in the city of Hebron in Judah, gathering his friends about him. If he wondered about his future, he had not long to wait, for soon the men of Hebron came to him and anointed him king of Judah.

For a time Abner, Saul's general, ruled the other tribes through a puppet king from Saul's family, but when he made a league with David, all the elders came to Hebron in Judah to declare David king of united Israel. When word of this reached the Philistines, they were aroused. A divided Israel was easy to control, but this was a different matter! They organized quickly to subdue David, but he was ready for them. With armies from all Israel under his able and inspiring generalship, it was not long before the Philistine power was broken. After that the Philistines were vassals of Israel and never again oppressed the country. The kingdoms of Moab and Edom across the Jordan also became subject to Israel, and treaties were made with other neighboring states.

David had had his eye for some time on the Canaanite stronghold of Jerusalem. It was in the center of the land between the tribes of the north and the tribes of the south. He conquered it, and then did something very statesmanlike. While he lived in Hebron of Judah, the northern tribes might think he was really only Judah's king. Now he moved his capital to Jerusalem, which was neutral territory. It was a wonderful place, high on the hills, and it became the center of his kingdom. David thought, "This kingdom is really the Lord's; therefore the Ark of the Covenant, the sign of his presence among us, must be at the chief city." Since the days when Shiloh was destroyed the Ark had not been set up in a central place, for when it was brought back by the Philistines it was put into a private home. Now David made plans for a great ceremony. He chose picked troops to accompany him, taking a cart specially made for the occasion, to bring the Ark in state to Jerusalem. The guard marched before it and also the musicians, playing on harps and psalteries and timbrels and cornets and trumpets. David himself wore the white linen garment of a priest, as much as to say, "The Lord is king and no one else." On entering Jerusalem, David expressed his joy by dancing before the Ark. His wife Michal was ashamed of him, but when she reproved him, he said, "It was before the Lord I danced, in thanks to him who made me ruler of the people of the Lord, the people of Israel." The Ark was carried into the Tabernacle and then David offered sacrifices of thanksgiving and blessed the people in the name of the Lord.

The people were happy to have the Ark set up in the Tabernacle again. David wanted to build a temple, but the prophet Nathan said: "Since the time Moses gave us the Ark and the Tabernacle, the Lord has walked among us. He has not had a fixed place for his dwelling. That has been his will. Besides, you have had so much war. The Lord says, 'Let your son who will be a man of peace build a temple.'" David was disappointed but he made preparations for the building, even though he was not to erect the Temple himself.

Although David earnestly desired to serve the Lord, he sometimes let himself be led astray by the evil practices of his time. When his wealth and power grew, so did the temptation to do wrong. He stayed at home idling when he might have been busy judging the people or leading his troops. He sinned grievously, taking the wife of one of his officers for himself and having that officer sent into the front line of battle, where he was killed. The people who knew what had happened were angry, for in Israel a king could not do just anything, as kings did in other lands. Then Nathan the prophet stepped forward. He told the king the story of a man—he let it seem as though it were one of the king's own subjects—a rich man who had taken the most prized possession of a poor man, a little pet lamb. David became angry and said, "As the Lord lives, the man who has done this thing shall surely die, because he had no pity!" Then Nathan said: "You are the man! Thus says the Lord God of Israel: 'I have anointed you king over Israel and saved you from death at Saul's hands. I have given you the people of Israel and the people of Judah to rule. Why have you despised the commandments of the Lord to do evil in his sight? You used the Ammonite army to kill Uriah, and you have taken his wife to be your wife.' " David bowed his head in shame. The prophet then told him what his punishment would be: the child of the new wife he had taken would die and there would be much trouble in his family from that time on.

The example of wickedness that David had given his sons brought much tragedy into his family and nation. David's much-loved son Absalom became so proud and ambitious that he organized a rebellion to take the throne from his father. When David's armies went out to quell the insurrection, he said to the commanders, "Deal gently for my sake with Absalom." But his wish was disregarded and Absalom was killed. David was broken-hearted. He mourned more over his son's death than over his treachery. "O Absalom, my son, my son!" he lamented. "Would to God that I had died for you!"

When the time came for David to die, he appointed his son Solomon his successor, saying: "Be strong and show yourself a man. Obey the law of the Lord your God, so that he may keep the promise he made me when he said, 'If your children walk in my ways with all their hearts, they shall stay on the throne of Israel.' "

Solomon had grown up at David's court during the years when Israel was becoming a prosperous nation, and he had lived an easy life. When he began to rule, he prayed for a wise and understanding heart so that he might rule the people with justice, but soon it appeared that what he really cared about was might and power. He built a magnificent Temple for the worship of the Lord God of Israel, for which the people were deeply grateful. Then he also built temples for the worship of the gods of Egypt and Moab and of Sidon and the Ammonites, to please the princesses from those countries whom he had married.

Solomon also developed trade with other countries. The wealth that came out of it was used to make Jerusalem magnificent, to build palaces and fortifications, to buy hundreds of chariots, and to keep a luxurious court, including a bodyguard who carried shields of gold. The people were dazzled when they saw all this display, but they had to pay too dearly for it not to be angered. They paid taxes that kept them always in debt. On occasion they were put to forced labor, all except Judah, whose burdens the king was inclined to make lighter. Soon the northern tribes became rebellious. Solomon was not interested in making the people contented, but in being a powerful king.

When Solomon died, the people came to his son Rehoboam and asked that he reduce their burdens. Rehoboam knew nothing about ruling over a people and he listened to bad counselors. So he said pompously: "Reduce your burdens? That I will not do. Rather will I increase your burdens. I will increase them greatly!" Then the people of the north elected Jeroboam for their king, a man who had been leader of a rebellion against Solomon. The people of Judah and Benjamin accepted Rehoboam as ruler because he was of David's family. When Rehoboam called on them to make war to force the northern tribes into his dominion, the prophet Shemaiah came and said: "The Lord has sent me to Rehoboam and to the people of Judah and Benjamin. He says: 'You shall not go to fight against your brothers. Return every man to his house, for this thing is from me.' " And all the people went home, for they knew, if the king did not, that the word of the Lord was to be obeyed more than the word of any king.

Now there were two kingdoms in the land. In the south Rehoboam ruled over Judah, which included Benjamin, and in the north Jeroboam was king over all the other tribes that made up the Kingdom of Israel.

VII. *"God . . . spake in time past unto the fathers by the prophets"*

FOR fifty years after the kingdom was divided there was bitterness and strife, but finally there came a time of peace. King Omri and his son Ahab had made the Northern Kingdom, Israel, a strong nation by worldly standards, but God had other plans for Israel. Thus the Bible writers make God's spokesman, the prophet Elijah, the hero of all this part of the nation's history. In later years many legends were told about Elijah, and the people of Israel always expected that he would come again to hold them to their course as the Lord's own people.

MANY prophets of the Lord had been killed and the rest were in hiding. King Ahab's steward brought bread and water to the caves where some had found refuge, but the steward did it without the king's blessing. Like David and Solomon, King Ahab was in league with the ruler of Phoenicia. To strengthen the union of the two countries, he had married the daughter of his ally. This daughter, Queen Jezebel, was behind all the trouble.

Queen Jezebel was not content, as Solomon's Egyptian queen had been, to confine the worship of her foreign god to her own royal court. Jezebel had much energy and she was a patriotic woman. Proud of the wealth and culture and power of her home city, she thought to herself: "These Israelites, not far removed from the bare life of the desert, how crude they are! And their god, what can he do? Baal of Tyre shall have dominion in this land. He shall become chief god here too!" Ahab the king was still loyal to the Lord God of Israel, but he was also devoted to the queen. Besides, Ahab did not see why various gods should not be worshiped in Samaria if the arrangement was good politics. So he did not interfere when Jezebel brought large numbers of Baal priests from her home and established them in the city of Samaria. The queen made it fashionable for people to worship with her, and in the many ways that would come to the mind of a clever and forceful queen she made it profitable also. Soon the worship of Baal of Tyre gained hold of Samaria and spread into all parts of the Kingdom of Israel. Some of the Israelites shrugged their shoulders and felt no pricks of conscience because they had forgotten the covenant of the Lord God. Others said, "After all, there isn't much difference!" for they belonged to groups that had grown up thinking they were serving the Lord God while they had been worshiping in the manner of the Canaanite Baal worshipers.

Among the many people of Israel who were outraged and deeply troubled by all this were the bands of prophets who were part of the life of Israel. They lived simple lives and were fiercely devoted to the Lord God and to his worship as they knew it. Up and down the country they preached, "It is the Lord's command, 'Thou shalt have no other gods before me.' " Jezebel was used to the worship of many gods under one chief god. "No other gods!" she said scornfully. "How dare they affront Baal of Tyre with such talk!" So she had the prophets slain—that is, all that she could lay hands on.

The kings of Israel were used to listening to the word of the Lord through the prophets, but Ahab thought that in this case the prophets were speaking only their own word and were mak-

ing an unnecessary disturbance. He wanted peace in the land,
and peace with Phoenicia, and he thought the prophets should
be grateful for peace. Still, he did not want to turn against the
prophets entirely. Therefore, he let it seem as though he did not
notice what was happening when his steward Obadiah took food
and drink to the persecuted prophets of the Lord.

Then suddenly, as if from nowhere, the prophet Elijah appeared before the king. In his rough garment of goat's hair he
stood fearlessly confronting the king and announced, "As surely
as the Lord God of Israel lives, there will be no rain or dew until
I give the word." Then before Ahab realized the meaning of the
message, Elijah was gone.

Ahab soon guessed what Elijah meant. Baal Melkarth of Tyre
and all the lesser gods were supposed to bring fertility and prosperity to the land. Their followers brought them sacrifices to
insure plentiful harvests. Elijah's message meant, "You shall see
whose power it is that gives us life in this land!"

The drought came. Month after month there was no rain. A
year passed, two years passed, and still no rain fell. As the food
became scarcer and scarcer, the people became more desperate.
At the Lord's command Elijah had been living in hidden places,
and Ahab sought him in vain. Then one day Elijah returned.
"Here is the one who has brought so much trouble to Israel!" said
the king. But Elijah answered, "It is not I who troubles Israel,
but you and your family!" Then he gave a command the king
dared not disobey: "Have all the people, including also the
prophets and priests of Baal who live at the expense of Jezebel,
gather on Mount Carmel!" Ahab sent his royal orders for the
gathering. The people and the prophets and priests of Baal
streamed to the high place, long held sacred, that was on the
promontory of Carmel, extending out into the Mediterranean
Sea.

Elijah rose before the people and said: "How long will you
keep on drifting between the worship of the Lord God and the
worship of Baal? If the Lord is God, follow him, but if Baal is
god, follow him!" The people did not answer. Then Elijah said:
"I alone am the Lord's prophet here. But there are four hundred
and fifty men who call themselves the prophets of Baal. Let

them prepare a sacrifice, and I will also prepare one. We will each lay our sacrifice upon wood, and put no fire under it. Call you all on the name of your gods. I will call on the name of the Lord God of Israel. The one who answers by fire, let him be God." Then the people said, "It is well spoken."

The priests and prophets of Baal prepared their sacrifice and called on their god, asking for fire. The whole day long they called, but there was no answer. They danced about the altar in a wild frenzy, but nothing happened. Elijah mocked them: "Cry louder, for perhaps your god is taking a walk or maybe he is having a nap." They took the mocking words for good advice and shouted the louder and cut themselves so that the blood flowed as they danced and cried. But the sacrifice lay cold on the altar as before.

Then Elijah said to the people, "Come over here to me!" They watched as he took stones to repair the altar of the Lord. When he had prepared the sacrifice, he poured water over it, and then he prayed. His great faith and earnestness held the people in reverence and expectation. "Lord God of Abraham, Isaac, and Israel, let it be known today that thou art God in Israel, and that I am thy servant, doing what thou hast bid me do. Hear me, O Lord. Hear me that this people may know that thou art God."

Then something happened that the people remembered as an act of God. Fire fell from heaven, the story says, and consumed the sacrifice. In awe the people fell on their faces and cried: "The Lord is God! It is the Lord who is God!" Elijah said: "This worship of Baal must be ended. Let none of the Baal prophets escape." So the people took them to the brook at the foot of the mountain and slew them. "If this is no land of Baal's," they reasoned, "his servants have no right to live in it." Like everyone else in his time, Elijah believed that the way to do away with wrong was to kill the wrongdoers.

The drought broke. There was thunder and lightning, and the rain poured down upon the thirsty land.

On the next day Elijah's courage failed. Jezebel had sent him word, "You shall pay with your life for the lives of the prophets of Baal." "I will die," he thought, "and my death will be in vain!" He had done what he had to do, but his action had not changed Jezebel, nor thousands of people the country over. In discouragement and fear, Elijah fled. After many days he came to Mount Horeb, where he hoped the Lord would make his presence known to him. Surely God would have to punish Israel for its faithlessness! Suppose Israel had lost the chance to be the Lord's people? Elijah knew he must learn the word of the Lord. He stood on the mountain, waiting for the Lord to speak to him.

A great storm came that shook the mountain. Had not God spoken since days of old through storm and wind? But no word came to Elijah out of the storm. He waited longer. There came an earthquake that broke the rocks of the mountain. But the Lord did not speak from the earthquake, nor did he speak in the fire that followed the earthquake. Then there came a deep silence. Elijah wrapped his mantle about his face, for he knew that the Lord was in the silence, speaking to him. "What are you doing here, Elijah?"

Elijah answered: "The people of Israel have forgotten their covenant with you and have thrown down your altars and killed your prophets. I am the only one left to serve you, and they are seeking to kill me too!" The Lord reassured Elijah: "There are thousands of quiet people in Israel who have never bowed their knees to Baal. You have known me in thunder and storm and lightning, but I work in quietness too, in the hearts of people. Go, return, there is much to do!"

Elijah went back among the people with new knowledge about God and his ways of working. He went also with a plan to anoint a new king of Syria who would be the Lord's instrument in punishing both the people of Israel and the king who had not learned to treasure loyalty to God more than prosperity. Baal worship did not stop, but it no longer swept the country, and the Lord's prophets were free again. However, Elijah found another task at hand.

It was expected in Israel that the king should treat his fellow countrymen as brothers. Although in other countries kings could defy the law and claim absolute authority over the citizens, in Israel it might not be so, for the Lord was king over all alike.

Ahab had a plan for enlarging the royal gardens around his palace at Jezreel, and to realize this dream he needed the ad-

joining property belonging to Naboth. So he went to his neighbor and offered to buy the vineyard or to give Naboth another
one as good as his own. Ahab thought the offer very reasonable,
but it happened that Naboth cared nothing for any vineyard except his own. This particular vineyard, inherited from his fathers
through all the generations they had lived in the land, was his
pride. Naboth did not expect the king to understand how much
he loved his own vineyard. It had had the loving and devoted
care of generations of his family. Fathers had planned with
sons how vines might be grafted to make them yield better grapes;
they had determined what new plants might be put in to bring
forth prized flavors for the grape harvest. If Naboth explained
all this, the king might not understand, but surely the king knew
that each Israelite had a right to the piece of ground he had
inherited! So Naboth said very briefly to Ahab, "The Lord forbid that I sell you the inheritance of my fathers." Ahab did not
argue, for he saw that his neighbor's decision was firm, but he
went home in a bad temper.

Jezebel noticed his black mood and was astonished that a king
would not insist upon getting what he wanted. When her father
in Phoenicia wanted anything, he could usually find a way to get
it! Why should a king of Israel be thwarted? So she said to Ahab:
"Let your heart be merry! I will get the vineyard for you!" She
then staged a mock trial where, on the testimony of false witnesses, Naboth was found guilty of blasphemy, for which the punishment was death by stoning. The sentence was carried out, and
Jezebel took her good news to Ahab: "The vineyard you wanted
is forfeited to you. Take possession of it, for Naboth is dead."

So Ahab went into the vineyard and took possession of it.
But his pleasure was brief, for soon Elijah appeared before him.
Angrily, Ahab exclaimed, "Have you found me, my enemy?"
Elijah answered: "I have found you, who have committed murder and also robbery. Thus says the Lord, 'Where dogs licked the
blood of Naboth, there will dogs lick your blood also. And the
throne shall be taken from your family.' " Ahab acknowledged
his guilt. He exchanged his royal robes for sackcloth and fasted
and sorrowed deeply. Because he repented, Elijah announced
that the punishment would be postponed, but not for long.

Trouble broke out between Syria and Israel. Although another brave prophet, Micaiah, warned Ahab not to go to war against the king of Syria, Ahab went. He sent Micaiah to prison, saying, "Stay there until I return victorious." But the battle went against Israel. Ahab was hit by an arrow and mortally wounded. The king's courage was apparent at his death, for, in spite of his wound, he stayed in his chariot among his troops until evening. His body was buried in Samaria, and when the chariot was washed out at the pool, dogs licked the blood, according to the words of the prophet.

Queen Jezebel was punished also, and with her the whole nation. Under the influence of Elijah and his successor Elisha, the throne of Israel was taken from Ahab's family. In a revolution led by Jehu, a captain in the army, Jezebel lost her life. The new king was forced to pay tribute to Assyria, a great new empire to the east that had been getting ever stronger. For years there was to be no peace for Israel as Assyria pushed its rule westward. But through all the sieges and famines and defeats, there were those in Israel who kept faith that God would finally bless them in a special way. They thought of this blessing as long life in a secure and strong nation, respected by other nations.

VIII. *"I desired mercy, and not sacrifice; and the knowledge of God more than burnt offerings"*

THE things that happened to Israel and Judah were interpreted for the people by the prophets and through them they learned even better what God was like and what he wanted them to do. When we read the stories of the prophets, we marvel that they understood so much and were so useful in God's plan.

THE day of the Lord is coming!" the people said to each other throughout Israel. "The day is coming when he will make his people glorious before all the world and his blessing will descend upon us in even greater fullness." At last there was peace, and, with peace, prosperity. It seemed to the people in both the Northern and Southern Kingdoms that a great future was dawning. The Assyrians, busy with troubles inside their borders, were not troubling Israel. Jeroboam II, who ruled over Israel, had subdued the neighbor nations. Rich booty from them and good trade with them brought wealth to Israel. The great caravan routes throughout the Jordan Valley were in Israel's control again, and goods from north, east, south, and west flowed through the country. "God is blessing us," the people said, "and why not? Are we not his people? Is he not our God who promised to bless us? Are we not bringing lavish offerings to his sanctuaries—even more than the law requires? Soon the great day will come when all our enemies and rivals will be at our feet." Thus spoke the comfortable ones in Israel.

When Amos, a herdsman from Tekoa, heard such talk, his blood rose, and he thought: "The day of the Lord indeed! The oppressed in the land don't see the day of the Lord coming!" When he thought of the farmers whose land, inherited from their forefathers, was being taken from them to be merged into big estates, and of fathers whose children were being sold into slavery, he said: "They don't feel blessed! They want freedom from the oppression of those who talk so proudly!"

Amos was an educated man and very well informed about all that was going on in the world and in his country. He had keen eyes and a sharp understanding, and he knew well the history of his people. He had thought and prayed much about God's purpose for Israel.

In his travels Amos had visited the markets of Israel in the north, and also the sanctuaries, where he had seen the priests in their splendid robes offering sacrifice to the music of viols and harps. He had watched the very people who oppressed the poor bringing sacrifices of animals, of fruits and grain and oil. As he strode along, mile after mile, on his way toward his home in the south, his mind was heavy with all that he had seen and heard.

In the market he had seen traders use false weights and measures that cheated the buyer. He had noticed how the price of a pair of shoes had been enough to bribe a judge to sell a man into slavery for a small debt. Amos had seen small landholders lose their inheritance to cruel men to whom they owed such debts. The judge in the courts had not been fair, but the bystanders had said, "If you don't have the price of a bribe, you have no chance!" When Amos remonstrated with such greedy and unjust people, the answer would come: "We have the law on our side! We are not transgressing the law!"

"How does all this appear to the Lord God?" Amos asked himself. In the simple life of the hills, in the clear open air where Amos herded his sheep, the corruption in the city seemed like a bad dream. What extravagant feasts with wild music he had observed! Those women in silken raiment who idled away their days on ivory couches in luxurious palaces—what did they care that their gorgeous jewelry was bought with money extorted from the poor? There was no more thought in their minds than in the head of a cow, no more understanding, no more justice and pity! "Cows of Bashan," Amos called them. And up and down the country, no justice in the courts! What was the Lord saying to it all? Could he endure it? The people would not learn justice and righteousness unless they suffered for their wrongdoing. Amos saw that clearly. Their sins would bring punishment upon them.

Then the word of the Lord came to Amos clearly and unmistakably: "Go, preach to my people Israel! Tell them that I hate and despise their sacred festivals, that I will not smell the smoke of their sacrifices of fat beasts. Tell them that I will not listen to their singing of hymns nor to the music of their instruments! Make clear my will that justice should well up in their midst like fresh water, and righteousness like a mighty stream!" And the Lord revealed to Amos the punishment he must proclaim.

Amos was a stern man, rugged and strong. But he had been living a quiet and lonely life, and he had not been trained in any of the schools of the prophets. "Must I really leave my herds and go among the people to preach?" he asked himself. But he knew he had heard aright, that the Lord had prepared him for just this task and was now sending him to carry his word. So he set out for Beth-el, the center of Israel's worship, to be there for the coming festival.

The people in their holiday garments were thronging the courts of the sanctuary. They were startled when suddenly they heard a man's voice raised above the crowd: "You say the day of the Lord is coming? It will be different from what you think! It will be a day of doom! It will be a day of darkness, and not a day of light!"

The worshipers stopped to listen, as they said to each other: "How does he dare? What does this rough herdsman mean?" Presently they applauded, for Amos was speaking of the sins of their rivals and enemies. "The Lord will punish all the nations for the evil they have done. The Philistines and the Phoenicians will he punish because they have sold their captives into slavery without mercy. He will punish the Ammonites because they were barbarously cruel in their warfare."

Amos knew what was in their minds as they showed their approval. "We Israelites shall be safe while our enemies are punished," they were thinking, "for we worship the Lord God. We are his own." But as Amos went on, his listeners stopped applauding. "The Lord will punish the heathen nations, not because they worship other gods, but because they have dealt wickedly with other people. The Lord rules over them too. Don't think that because he led you out of Egypt and redeemed you from slavery he had no one but you on his mind. He has no favorites! If you but knew it, he led the Philistines from Caphtor and the Syrians from Kir!" This completely new idea did not appeal to his audience. Were not they the Lord's chosen? How could any man question it? But Amos still went on.

"The Lord says: 'You are my people. You are my chosen, yes, but not chosen to do as you please. To you only have I made myself known, therefore I will punish you for all your sins. Because you know what is my will, your responsibility is great. You have trampled upon the poor. You have brought affliction to the righteous and just. You have taken bribes to keep the needy from their rights.'"

By that time, the chief priest Amaziah had learned about the crowd that was listening to Amos. He came in time to hear Amos tell the Lord's message condemning their worship: "God hates your wicked conduct and his command to Israel is, 'Let justice well up like fresh water, and let righteousness flow like a mighty stream!'" Almost too angry to listen, Amaziah heard Amos declare the punishment to come: "The Lord says he cannot longer overlook your iniquities. Israel will be led into captivity. This sanctuary and the others will be laid waste." Without delay Amaziah sent a messenger to the king in Samaria to say: "There is a

traitor speaking here. His words are bad for the people to hear!"
To Amos he said, without waiting for the king's order: "You seer
of visions! Go back to the land of Judah and make your living
there and prophesy there. Do not again prophesy here in Beth-el,
for this is the king's sanctuary. It is a royal house!

Amos was not frightened by Amaziah's words. "The Lord took
me as I followed the flock," he told the priest, "and the Lord said
unto me, 'Go, prophesy unto my people Israel.' Now therefore
you shall hear the word of the Lord. The Lord says that he will
destroy this sinful kingdom. Israel will be led away into exile."

No one dared lay hands on Amos, and he returned to his home.
Although he was banned from Beth-el, he did not stop preaching.
Even Beth-el had not heard the last of him, for Amos' messages
were put into writing. His scrolls circulated among the faithful
in both Israel and Judah.

The people were not dependent in those days upon Amos' messages alone for the word of the Lord. Another prophet arose
whose words the faithful in Israel treasured against the evil times
that were beginning to break upon the country. Hosea prophesied punishment because Israel had forsaken God, but he had
another message also.

He told a strange story of the way the Lord himself had prepared him to be his spokesman, for he knew that his life had been
guided by God. Hosea's wife had left him and was leading an
immoral life. But Hosea still loved her. When he learned later
that she had been sold into slavery, he bought her back and took
her into his home again. It was at this time that a great new understanding about God came to him. If a man, just a human being, could love and seek the welfare of one who had been unfaithful to him, would not the Lord God still have mercy in his heart
for the people of Israel, even though they had been untrue to him?

The people asked Hosea: "Are you sure the Lord will not cast
us off? You know how Amos prophesied that our nation would
be destroyed!"

Hosea answered: "Indeed, punishment must come, but it is
God's way of winning Israel back. It is his way of making Israel
truly his own. He will not cast off his people!"

Hosea could not forget how the Israelites had given themselves to the worship of Baal. He said: "Israel has been untrue to the Lord and has gone after Baal. There must be punishment for Israel's injustice and rebellion. But when all these troubles are over, the people will no more mention the name of Baal. Israel will know the will of the Lord and will live in righteousness and loving-kindness before him. Through all the sufferings that are to come, God is leading us into a future when Israel will be reconciled to him and will say, 'Thou art our God,' and he will say, 'You are my people.' "

The people of Israel needed all the comfort they could get from Hosea's words. Assyria, the great empire to the east, wanted to conquer the world; Egypt, to the southwest, although weak, was not ready to give up dreams of world empire. Therefore, the smaller countries between, including Palestine, were caught in almost continual wars. Strife and violence and corrupt government had made the country weak, for after the death of Jeroboam II there had been no stable government in Israel. One usurper after another had taken the throne of Israel by murdering the reigning king. In the Southern Kingdom, Judah, conditions had been better than in Israel, but there also evils had sapped the strength of the nation.

The Assyrians came marching from the north and were bought off, for the time being, by a huge tribute of a thousand talents of silver. The people of Israel were frightened by the threat of the enemy's cruelty, for Assyria had a policy of resettling its conquered peoples in lands away from home. Israel was made desperately poor by continued demands for tribute. Some of the Israelites, not realizing Assyria's great might, believed they could fight off the enemy, and one of them, Pekah, made himself king. He joined with Rezin of Syria to get the support of the Kingdom of Judah in the south for a revolt against the Assyrian overlord.

The thoughtful ones in Israel knew that the day of judgment was near, the day of doom which Amos and Hosea had foretold. They treasured Hosea's teaching that God's judgments are just and at the same time merciful: "The punishments God sends are his way of making Israel more truly his own people." They remembered how Amos had said, "Perhaps the Lord will save a remnant, if you love the good and hate the evil."

IX. *"The Lord our God is holy .... Walk humbly with thy God"*

ISAIAH, who prophesied in Judah, knew the righteousness of God as did Amos and Hosea. More clearly than they he proclaimed the majesty and holiness of the one God who rules over all the nations of the world.

KING AHAZ and his counselors were so frightened that they trembled. They were inspecting Jerusalem's water supply to learn how well the city might withstand a siege. Ahaz had just refused to have his kingdom of Judah join in a revolt against Assyria. Pekah of Israel and Rezin of Syria were sure that if all the kingdoms in Palestine and Syria united their strength, they could resist the armies of Assyria successfully. But Ahaz had said to them: "It will only make matters worse to fight now. Assyria is too strong for us." Then word had come that the kings of Israel and Syria were on the way with their armies to dethrone Ahaz and to force the people of Judah to join them against Assyria.

"We cannot withstand them—our army is too small against those of Israel and Syria combined!" the terrified king said to his council. Then a foolhardy plan took shape in King Ahaz' mind. He would send a message to Tiglath-pileser, the Assyrian conqueror-king, to say that Pekah and Rezin were plotting against Judah and Assyria. King Ahaz knew that in return for help against his two small neighbor nations he would become a vassal of the Assyrian king, who wanted to rule the world.

Now the word of the Lord came to a young prophet named Isaiah. Isaiah knew that the Lord God was ruler of all the earth and not just God of the territory occupied by Israel and Judah. Therefore, nothing like armies or horses and chariots or kings and empires could frighten him. What troubled him deeply was to see oppression of the poor, and dishonesty and bribery, in the land. He knew that a holy God must punish unrighteousness. He loved his nation dearly and mourned over its evil ways. When he despaired of the whole nation, God assured him that a remnant of his people would be saved.

King Ahaz knew how Isaiah felt about doing God's will. Everybody knew. Often Isaiah had preached about it; he had even sung about it in the streets to make the people listen; and he had written his messages from God on scrolls for the people to read. They were reminded too by the strange name he had given his little boy. Shearjashub was his name, meaning "a remnant shall return." When people saw the child or heard his name called, it was like a warning to them: "Not all of us will live to be truly God's people—only a few." But the name told them God's promise too. When the people saw the child they were reminded: "A part of the nation will be saved to live righteously as God's people. God has not forsaken us!"

Isaiah felt prompted by the Lord to go to the king, who was in conference with his counselors beside the reservoir. So he took his little boy by the hand, and together they set out to bring confidence and advice to the king, who was much too frightened to be as wise as was needful. The king was glad to see Isaiah coming along with his child, for he knew the prophet's common sense and courage. But he was not glad to hear what Isaiah had to say.

"Be quiet in your mind!" Isaiah said to the king. "Pekah of

Israel and Rezin of Syria have no strength. They cannot hold out. They are just flickering torches that will soon be burned out. Indeed, in a few years both those kings will lose their thrones and both those nations will be nations no more. Be quiet and have confidence in the Lord. You say your army is not strong. In quietness and confidence will be your strength."

This did not sound practical to the king. Isaiah could see that it did not, therefore he put a question to him to test him: "Ask a sign of the Lord! Anything! Ask a sign!" The king demurred. "I will not tempt the Lord and ask a sign!" Isaiah knew that it was not humility, but rather disobedience to God, that the king was showing. Therefore he became angry and said to Ahaz: "The kings of Israel and Syria will soon lose their thrones as I have told you, but that judgment upon them will not turn aside God's judgment upon a rebellious Judah."

King Ahaz rather envied Isaiah's faith in God, but he had none himself. Tiglath-pileser, of the Assyrian Empire, who ruled in the great city of Nineveh, seemed a safer reliance right now. On his return to the palace, the king sent this message to Nineveh: "Pekah of Israel and Rezin of Syria are conspiring against you and against me. Come and help!"

The Assyrians came. They carried out orders to take Rezin from his throne and make an end of his Syrian kingdom. Pekah of Israel was dethroned also and a puppet king put in his place. Many of the people were carried away captive. King Ahaz and his people in Judah paid heavily for the intervention. If Ahaz had not aroused the Assyrians, the little Judean country in the hills might have been overlooked for a long time. Instead, its independence was lost. Ahaz had to pay a heavy tribute of silver and gold from the Temple and palace treasuries, and besides he had to tax the people for further tribute. Judah became a subject nation.

What caused most sorrow to the faithful worshipers of the Lord God was the new kind of worship that spread over the land, for Assyria expected its vassal nations to worship its gods and follow its customs in their sanctuaries. King Ahaz had a new altar erected in the Temple at Jerusalem, patterned after the altars of the Assyrian gods. Throughout Judah symbols of Assyrian sun

and star worship appeared at the sacred places. Many liked the
new ways. It seemed fashionable and smart to be part of so great
an empire.

So the years went by, and the warnings of Amos and Hosea
were forgotten. Many of the people in both Israel and Judah were
sure that soon better days would come. But always there were
some who knew that if the nation did not repent of its evil ways
new disasters would be its lot.

Then one day even the thoughtless ones were shaken out of
their dream that all was well. Messengers came from the Northern Kingdom with terrible news. The Kingdom of Israel was no
more! The Assyrian armies had come again to quell another revolt. After a long siege, the city of Samaria had fallen. Thousands
of the citizens of Israel had been taken from their homes and were
on the way to be settled in other parts of the Assyrian Empire.
Strangers from other rebellious countries were being brought to
Palestine in their place. The day of doom foretold by Amos had
come. Now the hopes of all the children of Israel to be a nation
specially blessed of God centered in the Kingdom of Judah. And
Judah was following other gods!

Isaiah said to himself: "The blow has fallen upon unrighteous
Israel, and it is only a matter of time until it will fall on Judah as
well. But God's purpose will never, never fail!"

He called a group of disciples about him and they talked together of the ways of God with his people. "The Lord has not
brought us this far only to abandon us to ruin. He will yet establish a people who are truly his own. A remnant will be saved
through whom the blessing will come," Isaiah taught them.

"What if kings keep betraying their people," the disciples
questioned, "as even our king of David's line has betrayed us?"
Isaiah assured them, "Because of the zeal of the Lord himself,
there will one day come a king in whom the Spirit of God dwells,
a son of David who will rule in righteousness and justice and
peace."

A new excitement stirred the country. Hezekiah had come to
the throne, a wiser man than Ahaz, but influenced by the general
feeling that it would be good to join Egypt in a revolt against
Assyria. It was known that Assyria was weakened by strife within,

that people in many places had become desperately tired of its overlordship. But the people of Judah did not know how weak Egypt was. The streets, the market places, and the Temple courts buzzed with talk of alliance with Egypt. "It would be a good thing!" "Anything is better than being slaves to Assyria!"

Then someone called: "Have you seen the prophet Isaiah in captive's garb? He is walking through the streets barefoot!" Crowds gathered about him as he preached. "If only you would trust in the Holy One and live righteously instead of trusting in Egypt and its chariots and horsemen! The Egyptians are men, and not God; their horses are flesh, and not spirit! You cannot rely upon them! In quietness and confidence is strength!"

Some people laughed. Others were scornful. Most of them just shook their heads. Only a few believed as the prophet did. Day after day he walked about barefoot and wearing only a loincloth, which was the garb of a slave. He did not need to say in words: "You will go into captivity like your brothers in the north. That is what Assyria does, sends its rebels into captivity. Why hasten the day by a foolish alliance with Egypt?"

The king gave in to the citizens and made a pact with Egypt, Chaldea, and some other nations that were rebelling against Assyria. At a festival in Jerusalem the people sang and shouted on the roofs as they watched a parade in the streets below. Isaiah grieved to see them joyful, for he knew that even then the Assyrian armies were descending upon them. The Assyrians devastated the country, burning town after town, until King Hezekiah surrendered. He had to pay huge tribute, all the gold and silver that could be found in the palace and Temple treasuries. He thought the enemy was satisfied, but instead the Assyrian army appeared before Jerusalem, surrounding its walls and demanding surrender.

The people in the city were in despair. The deputy of the Assyrian king, who commanded the army, suspected that the Judeans were not altogether happy, so he thought of a clever scheme. He planned to take this fortress on the heights without a siege. He was going to talk the people of Jerusalem into surrender. In Assyria they were forever dethroning kings and putting new ones on the throne. Unaware of the loyalty of the people of Judah to their kings of David's line, he planned to put his knowledge of their language to very good use. So he called for a deputation to come out on the walls to hear him, and then he made a speech, very loudly, using the Hebrew language so that any in range of his voice might understand him.

"My message is to the people, not to the king," he called. "Set aside your king. Come over to us and pledge yourselves to the king of Assyria. Do not listen to Hezekiah when he says, as I have heard he does, 'The Lord God will deliver us.' Assyria is too strong for your god! Were the gods of any of the other countries strong enough to save them from Assyria? They were not. Shall I count them for you?" He counted them up, quite a list, almost all the countries the people on the walls or in the city knew anything about. Then he went on: "If the gods of all these countries were not strong enough to save their lands, how can you believe that your god can save you from the Assyrian might? Give in peaceably and I will take you to a country where you will have bread and vineyards and olives and honey, where you will live and not die. But don't say, 'The Lord will deliver us!' "

The men of Judah answered no word but brought the message of the Assyrian deputy to King Hezekiah. The king rent his garments in sorrow and hastened into the Temple to pray. He sent messengers to Isaiah, asking that he pray also. Isaiah said: "Indeed, the Lord has used the Assyrians against us to punish us and Jerusalem does not deserve to be saved. But may an ax boast against the one who uses it? Assyria may not mock the Lord! Take this answer to the king: 'Thus says the Lord, "The Assyrians shall not come into the city nor shoot an arrow into it, for I will defend the city to save it!" ' "

In the morning, when the citizens of Jerusalem looked down from their walls, they saw a deserted camp. The besieging army had departed. Some reports say that a rumor had come of revolt at home; others, that a plague had broken out in the army so that thousands died. At any event, the army was gone. The faithful said, "Our enemies were smitten by an angel of the Lord!" for they knew God had delivered them.

Isaiah wrote a poem of gratitude to God. He thought that now the people would certainly repent. Surely now they would know

God's care for them and would want to do what was right. Surely now they had seen the greatness of the Holy One who could not excuse evil. "The whole earth is full of his glory," he said. "How can man not be in awe of him?" But the people replied, "Let us eat, drink, and be merry, for tomorrow we die!" Although Isaiah was greatly disappointed, he did not despair. The Lord would yet bring it about that they would know Him and live after his ways.

Isaiah was an aged man by the time Manasseh came to rule. By that time the king and the masses of the people worshiped after the manner of the Assyrians and of the Babylonians who were rising in power. Many of those who insisted upon serving the Lord God were killed as traitors. Poverty and injustice and fear of the future weighed heavily upon the people. Isaiah assured his disciples that a better time would come. "The knowledge of God will cover the earth, as the waters cover the sea, and all the earth will be at peace." This was their hope. Because of it they kept faith, although there was no sign of peace anywhere.

After Isaiah died, those whom he had taught kept on studying his writings and the writings of the other prophets. The newest of the books was one written by the prophet Micah. Micah had known the countryside of Judah in the way Isaiah knew Jerusalem. He told how the people in town and in country had asked him: "What can we do to please God that he may stop punishing us? Perhaps he will be good to us again if we do as the heathen and offer our first-born children. Is that what he wants?" Micah had answered: "You know what is good and what the Lord requires—not thousands of rams, nor ten thousand rivers of oil, and surely not your children. What he requires is that we deal justly with each other and love mercy and that we live in quiet fellowship with him."

Some of the faithful sat down to write another book, about something they believed to be a matter of life and death for their countrymen to know. Through the history of their people and the word of the prophets, they had learned that a nation that disobeys God's commands destroys itself. So they wrote a book in which they told the secret of life and death which they had discovered: "Obey God and live; disobey and the result is destruction." It was a book of laws interpreting the law of God, and when it was finished they hid it in the Temple for safekeeping. There it stayed through all the wicked reign of Manasseh and the reign of his son.

More than eighty years later, when the good king Josiah ruled the land of Judah and had the Temple cleaned and repaired, the book was found. When it was read to the king, he tore his robe in sorrow and called his counselors to hear the reading.

"Listen to this from the book," he said. "The book of the law says, 'Hear, O Israel, the Lord our God is one God,' but our people are worshiping many gods. 'There shall be no poor among the Lord's people,' it says. 'In the olive harvest, do not beat down all the olives from the trees but leave some on the branches for the poor and the stranger. In the wheat harvest leave the gleanings for the poor and the stranger to pick up. Look after the widows and orphans.' But in our land we take away from the poor even the little that they have. Our courts are full of bribery, while the book says, 'The judge shall hear the small and the great alike, for the Lord is just,' and it warns us that the punishment of the Lord will come upon those who do not live according to these laws."

To Hilkiah the priest and to Shaphan the scribe the king gave the command, "Go, inquire if this book is truly the word of the Lord," and they asked the prophetess Huldah. She answered, "It is truly the word of the Lord, and the anger of the Lord is great against us." Then the king called a meeting of the people in the courts of the Temple and had the book read to them. The people promised before God that all the altars in the land should be torn down, that the Temple in Jerusalem alone should be their holy place, and that all the laws in the book should be obeyed.

The faithful in the land were jubilant when the new covenant was proclaimed. They thought: "Now that we have good laws, the people will be good. Surely when the sanctuaries with their heathen manner of worship are no more, the people will worship the Lord."

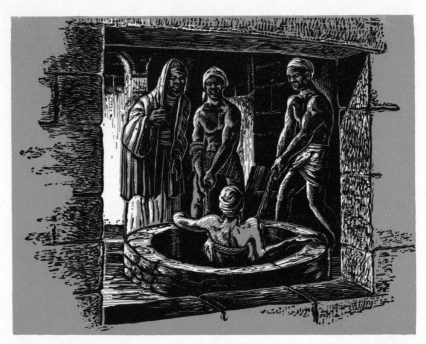

X. *"This shall be the covenant that I will make with the house of Israel; . . . saith the Lord, I will put my law in their inward parts, and write it in their hearts"*

IN THE ages past it was taken for granted that God needed the whole of the nation of Israel for the achievement of his purpose. Isaiah came to believe that a remnant could fulfill the task. To Jeremiah was revealed the importance to God of each single individual. He is often thought of as "the prophet of woe," but when the time of doom came it was through his confident hope that the remnant were saved from utter despair.

NINEVEH has fallen! Nineveh is burning to the ground! We need fear the Assyrians no longer, for their empire is no more!" This was the news that caused rejoicing in all the small nations, including those in Palestine. But what seemed peace was not really peace. The great city of Babylon was the center of the new empire that had conquered Assyria. Babylon, like Assyria, expected all the small nations to be its vassals. The people of Judah paid little heed. Was not Josiah, descendant of their great King David, a king who served the Lord? Surely they could depend upon the Lord to defend them if enemies should arise! They were the people of the law! The Lord must be pleased with their worship now that the altars of other gods were all torn down.

The prophet Jeremiah shocked them when he proclaimed: "Your hopes are false. Jerusalem will be destroyed!" and roused their fury against him. These things happened after Jeremiah had been a prophet for many years. He was not so bold when he first began. In fact, he was a gentle young man then, even timid, and he resisted the call to be the Lord's prophet. The story of how he became a prophet is recorded in a book which he himself wrote. The word of the Lord came to him, saying, "Before ever you were born I knew you and set you apart to be a prophet to the nations." Then Jeremiah answered, "O Lord God, behold, I cannot speak in your name, for I am a child!" But the Lord told him that he was not too young or inexperienced. He said to Jeremiah, "Do not say, 'I am a child,' for you shall go to all to whom I shall send you, and whatever I command, you shall speak."

The first task that came to Jeremiah was to proclaim in the towns of Judah and in the streets of Jerusalem the laws the people had agreed to accept in the reform instituted by King Josiah. "Listen to the terms of the law and obey them," he called, and he read among other statutes the one that called for the abolishment of all the local shrines. In the course of destroying the sacred places the reformers came to Jeremiah's home town of Anathoth near Jerusalem. They tore down the sanctuary where the people had been accustomed to celebrate their festivals and their Sabbaths and to bring their sacrifices. The citizens of Anathoth had no mind to accept the change, and their anger was roused against Jeremiah. "Raised in our own town, and he sides with those reformers from Jerusalem! He would have us give up our shrine and go all the way to the Temple for sacrifices!"

Jeremiah believed the change was necessary and right but he could also understand how his people felt. They could no longer worship in heathenish ways at the village shrine; that was good, but it was a disadvantage that they could no longer worship in their home community, sharing their happy times and their sad times at the village sanctuary in the way they had done since days of old. He understood the sorrow of his kinsmen even though he was partly responsible for it, but they felt only anger against him and plotted to kill him. "His name shall not be remembered among us," they said.

Jeremiah escaped, and the Lord sent him to Jerusalem to endure something even more trying than the enmity of his home village. On the way, when his heart was heavy because of the anger of his friends and relatives, he asked God why he should have to endure such unhappiness. God's answer warned him that things would not be easier but rather harder in Jerusalem. He heard God saying to him, "If you have run with footmen and they have wearied you, how can you contend with horses?" which was as much as to say, "My dear Jeremiah, if you can't bear it that your village rejects you, how can you triumph in the great struggle that is before you in Jerusalem?"

That city was a very discouraging place. Jeremiah saw every kind of superstition. The people trusted in household gods and idols to ward off danger; they consulted wizards and practiced magic. He said to himself: "These are the poor and unlettered. They have never learned what their religion means. I will go to the learned, to the leaders in the city, and will speak to them." He thought they would help him speak the Lord's word to the people, but he found that their worship was an empty set of forms and that truth and justice were nothing to them.

Presently, after the fall of Nineveh, conditions became much worse. The kindly king Josiah, who had judged the poor and needy righteously and who cared about true worship, dared to oppose the Pharaoh of Egypt. Pharaoh was on his way northward with his army to seize the lands of Palestine and Syria before the Babylonians could take control of them. Josiah tried to block the Egyptians at Megiddo and lost his life. All the people who wished for the good of the nation mourned him. Jeremiah grieved over him, and wrote in his book, "For the hurt of my people I am hurt."

King Josiah's son Jehoahaz succeeded his father on the throne at Judah. The new king had reigned for only three months when Pharaoh sent him to Egypt in chains and put his brother Jehoiakim, another son of Josiah, on the throne as his vassal. The new king gave no thought to the poor and the needy; he paid no attention to the bribery that was going on in the courts. He lived in a luxurious palace, with cedar ceilings painted a gaudy vermilion, which he had built by forced labor.

The fickle population forgot the promises they had made to deal justly with one another and to have nothing to do with heathen worship. Their one Temple in Jerusalem, with its large corps of priests, went back to the manner of worship that had been learned from Assyrian overlords and from Canaanite inhabitants of the land. So long as it was worship in the Temple, it was in their minds the worship of the Lord God.

Poverty was great, and the needs of the poor and the stranger were forgotten. As in Amos' day, the greedy and selfish thought the sacrifices in the Temple set them right with God. Although they felt the threat of the enemy, they were confident. Were they not God's people? Their nation and their city and Temple were safe in God's care, for had they not been saved from the enemy in Isaiah's day? And would not the Lord be faithful to his covenant? Other preachers in the country proclaimed, "We have the Temple of the Lord; therefore we are safe." But Jeremiah knew that the Temple worship, although elaborate and well attended, had become too corrupt to be worth preserving. The popular preachers said, "We are God's people, for we have the law of Moses," but Jeremiah knew that good laws did not make people good if hearts were not obedient to a holy and righteous God.

At this time, the word of the Lord came to Jeremiah, telling him to speak to the people at the gate of the Temple. When they came from the towns and farms and vineyards of Judah for the festival service, he was to speak all the words God would command him to say to them. Jeremiah appeared at the Temple gate, where the crowds were assembled, and in the name of the Lord told them the astounding and, they thought, traitorous prophecy that their nation and Temple would be destroyed unless they repented.

"Hear the word of the Lord, all you of Judah who enter these gates to worship the Lord! You keep saying, and hearing your preachers say, 'This is the Lord's Temple, his very own Temple; we are safe because we have the Lord's Temple.' But the Lord says: 'You have made my house into a robbers' den. You steal and murder and commit adultery, you perjure yourselves and wander after other gods, and then you come to present yourselves before me in this my house, thinking you are safe to go on with your wickedness. Do you remember how the sanctuary at Shiloh in the north was destroyed? This Temple is no safer. I will do to this house, which is called by my name and in which you trust, as to Shiloh, and all the land shall be desolate.' "

There were some faithful servants of the Lord who knew that Jeremiah's message was true. But the throngs of worshipers and the priests and false prophets and the officers of the court would not accept it. To them Jeremiah was a traitor. "This man deserves death, for he has prophesied against this city," they shouted.

Jeremiah repeated his words: "This is a message from the Lord. You can still repent and live." And he added: "What you do with the messenger is not important, so long as you hear the message. I am in your hand. Do with me as seems good to you."

Then they knew that Jeremiah was speaking truly in the Lord's name, and the leaders and the people said to one another: "This man does not deserve death. He has spoken to us in the name of the Lord our God." This time they let Jeremiah go his way. But when again he spoke the same words of warning, they put him into the stocks at the city gate and derided him. "He says we will be destroyed," they mocked, "but we will outlive him!" None of them understood how great was Jeremiah's grief that his own people whom he loved would be exiles.

The people who persecuted him and sought to keep him in prison seemed to be prospering in their affairs, and Jeremiah doubted for a time that the Lord was governing the world justly "Why do wicked people prosper?" he asked the Lord. "And how can it be that people who deal treacherously with others may live at ease?" Sometimes he was overcome with anger against his tormentors and he prayed, "O Lord, remember me, and come to me, and avenge me against my persecutors."

Always the Lord's command and Jeremiah's love for his people sent him back to warn them. He dared to tell the king that it was unlawful to use forced labor for the building of his palace. Then he had to go into hiding, for his life was in danger. The word of the Lord came to him: "Take a scroll and write," and so, with the help of his young disciple and scribe Baruch, he used the time when he was in hiding to put his messages from the Lord into writing. Then he sent Baruch to read them in the court of the Temple when many were assembled for a day of fasting. The enemy's power was gaining. The people were anxious to win God's favor. "Perhaps," thought Jeremiah, "they will heed the reading of my message although they would not listen to my spoken word."

The only person who paid much attention was the grandson of Shaphan, the scribe who in King Josiah's day had brought the Book of the Law to the king's notice. This influential man told some of the princes and officials of Jeremiah's scroll, and asked Baruch to read it to them. They listened with respect and were filled with anxiety and alarm, but they put the scroll away safely and advised Baruch to stay in hiding with his master lest the king be angrier still. The king heard about the scroll and sent one of his courtiers to bring it and read it to him. Warming himself as he sat beside a fire burning in a brazier, the king listened, but he showed his contempt of the warnings by cutting off the scroll as it was read, and burning it piece by piece in the fire. Then Jeremiah in his hiding place heard the Lord's command to write another scroll, and with Baruch's help he set to work at once.

After the fall of Assyria and then of Egypt, Babylonia ruled all of western Asia. King Jehoiakim of Judah had to pay tribute to Nebuchadnezzar, king of Babylon. After several years he rebelled, but he himself died before the rebellion brought disaster to the people and to his young son Jehoiachin, who succeeded him. The armies of the Babylonian ruler appeared before the city of Jerusalem. On orders of Nebuchadnezzar, the king and his court were taken captive, and also the leading priests of the Temple, the fighting men, the skilled workmen with their families, and the landowners. All these filed through the gates of the fallen city, exiles from their country. The rest of the people were left leaderless except for Zedekiah, the well-meaning but weak son of

Josiah, appointed king by Nebuchadnezzar. The people were near despair. Jeremiah, suffering deeply with them, asked, "What is the Lord telling us by these things that are happening?" The answer came to him: "The people who have had to leave their home and country are not deserted by the Lord. They have lost their homes to gain a better knowledge of the Lord and his will. Away from their Temple, in a strange land, they will learn to think highly of the things that really matter. They will return knowing better than before how the Lord has revealed himself through all their history."

After a time word came that the exiles were being treated well in Babylon, and that they were permitted to worship in the ways of their people. Jeremiah sent a letter to them, saying: "Know that the Lord has given me a message for you. Use the liberty that is given you. Build houses and plant gardens, establish family life, and make yourselves at home in Babylon. Do not trust the prophets who say that you will return speedily, but know that the Lord will surely bring back your descendants. The Lord thinks thoughts of peace concerning you and not thoughts of evil. Do not regard the Babylonians as enemies and conquerors and turn yourselves against them. They also are in the Lord's care. It is your duty to seek the welfare of the city in which you live and to pray to the Lord for it. You are not away from the Lord's presence, though you are away from his Temple. 'You shall seek me, and find me,' says the Lord, 'when you shall search for me with all your heart.'"

Many of the exiles were comforted and guided by the letter, but some were outraged and sent a protest to Jerusalem. They thought that a prophet should be arrested who dared say that the captivity would be long and who advised them to submit to the enemy.

There seemed to be no leaders in Jerusalem who could guide the affairs of the nation wisely. It should have been apparent that further rebellion would bring only war and famine and pestilence, but the crowds flocked to the popular prophets who said nothing about wickedness and who proclaimed: "You will not see sword nor famine. The Lord will give you peace in this place. You shall not serve the king of Babylon." Jeremiah said: "It breaks my heart to hear these prophets! If the people would listen to the word of the Lord, they would know that the Lord's word is like a fire, like a hammer that breaks the rocks in pieces, and not the easy, pleasant thing one would like to hear." He became more and more unpopular, until at last he was tempted to keep still. "I will speak no more the Lord's word," he said to himself. But he could not stop; God's word became like a burning fire in him and he had to speak.

There came a time again when Jeremiah was considered a traitor. The Babylonians were besieging Jerusalem but had withdrawn a little distance when they heard that the Egyptians were coming to the help of the city. When one day Jeremiah left Jerusalem to visit his home in Anathoth, people thought that he was deserting to the Babylonian camp and he was arrested on the charge of treason. He spent some time in prison, but later the leaders sent a demand to the king that he be put to death. King Zedekiah did not know how to resist the demand. Eventually he gave orders for Jeremiah to be thrown into a miry pit to die of starvation. However, an Ethiopian, servant of the king, rescued him from the pit and put him into the court of the prison instead, where he lived until the city fell. For it did fall. The Babylonian army, after defeating the Egyptian forces, came against the city once more and besieged it. The people would have been desperate and without hope, but Jeremiah told them over and over: "The time of trial is but a time of testing. The Lord still loves his people."

The city fell, and the Temple was burned. The other prophets could only say: "The Lord has forsaken us. The covenant is broken." But Jeremiah said, "The Lord's word to you is this: 'I have loved you with an everlasting love. I will build you again, and you shall be built, O people of Israel, and I will forgive your sins. After seventy years you will return.'"

After a month of plundering in the city the army departed, taking with them into captivity in Babylon King Zedekiah, his family, the court, and the remaining priests and leaders. Jeremiah was given his choice and decided to stay with the poor people who remained to till the fields. A governor was left in charge, but presently he was murdered. In fear of further punishment at the hands of the king of Babylon, a company of the people decided to flee to Egypt, forcing the aged Jeremiah to go with them. They treated him as if his warning had been the cause of the evil days that were upon his people.

Tradition says that in their anger at Jeremiah's counsel and warnings his countrymen stoned him. Years later his people knew that none in their history had spoken more clearly the word of the Lord than had Jeremiah, who alone had seen the Lord's intention with his people. He had dreamed of a time when they would not have to depend upon land, or law, or Temple to represent the Lord's presence to them, but would have his Spirit in their hearts. "Behold, the days come," Jeremiah had said in the Lord's name, "that I will make a new covenant. I will put my law in their inward parts, and in their heart will I write it."

XI. *"As the heavens are higher than the earth,*
so are my ways higher than your ways, and
my thoughts than your thoughts, . . ."
saith the Lord

THE great empires of the world were still striving against one another as they had done for many long years. For a time the people of Judah, in captivity in Babylonia, were not aware of the turmoil in the world. What happened to them during this time happened mostly in their thoughts and feelings, in their hearts and minds.

HOMESICK, are they? How can they live in this prosperous country and be homesick for a ruined Temple and a desolate city!" Thus the proud Babylonian neighbors exclaimed when they noted the sorrow of the captives who had come with their king, Zedekiah, from Judah. To all appearances they were comfortably settled under their own elders in the colonies assigned to them in Babylonia.

77

As far as the eye could see the land was like a great garden. Instead of the spare hills of Judah, the exiles saw fruitful plains. The irrigation canals were lined with fruit and palm and willow trees. The waterways were as busy with traffic as were the roads of the great merchant empire. High walls and towers and hanging gardens, colossal temples with tall portals, all told the might of the land of which Babylon was capital. But this great prosperous country was not home, and the Judean homeland was in ruins.

Worst of all, the exiles felt forsaken of God. They remembered Jeremiah's letter and how he had assured them of God's care. Still, had not all the prophets warned that God would cast them off if they broke the covenant? "God has abandoned us," they thought. "It may even be that he has no power in this strange country." So when they gathered by the waterways to sing songs of their homeland, they wept instead, and hung their harps on the willow trees.

Some of the people of Judah forgot their sorrow quickly because for them it was not a great sorrow. They had never really worshiped God in their homeland; therefore it was easy to forget him now. While working as farmers and gardeners and traders and builders among the Babylonians, they began to adopt the customs of the land and its ways of worship. The faithful among the people of Judah, those who treasured their laws and tried to live in obedience to God, were still more saddened when they saw this disloyalty. The Babylonian worship outraged them. "It is an abomination to our God!" they exclaimed. Then their doubts rose again. "Our God, we say? Is he still our God?"

"There is a prophet among us who can help you, as he helped us," said some of the people who had come into exile eleven years earlier. With them had come Ezekiel, a member of one of the priestly families. "The Lord told Ezekiel to be a watchman and a shepherd of his people. He knows what the Lord is saying. Come with us and speak with him."

So they went to Ezekiel, the prophet of the Lord. Ezekiel sorrowed too. The wife whom he loved had died at the time the Temple in Jerusalem had been burned, the Temple that had been his pride. Here was a man stricken in sorrow, who still knew the Lord's word. So they told him the despair that was upon them.

"You have seen the worship that goes on in the great temples of the Babylonians," they said, "how it is full of wickedness. Yet have not the Babylonians destroyed our Temple? Does that not mean their gods are greater than our God?"

Ezekiel could hardly find words to tell of the majesty and greatness and holiness of the Lord. "It is because the Lord our God is holy and we were wicked that our doom came. The gods of Babylonia are nothing, and Babylonia will one day suffer for its sins. Read what the prophets have said."

The people had no temple in which they could offer sacrifice to God, but they learned a new way to worship. They offered sacrifice by fasting. They also came together to study the scrolls they had carried with them.

Together they read the words of Amos and Hosea and Micah and Isaiah. All the prophets had spoken like Jeremiah, saying that doom was coming because of disobedience to God's commands. "We know that we fall far short of all that our forefathers promised in the covenant," the exiles said to Ezekiel. "If it is true that the Lord cannot abide sin, then he has surely forsaken us. We have broken the covenant, and are therefore not his people any more."

Ezekiel said to them: "The Lord punishes the sinner that he may return from his evil ways and do right. Return to him and he will forgive you." They searched their scriptures again and were comforted to see how Hosea, and Isaiah too, had told of the Lord's mercy.

More questions came to these faithful ones who wanted to be sure of God's justice. "Why should we suffer so much? We have no idols. We do not worship the Babylonian gods the way our forefathers worshiped Canaanite gods. It was our forefathers who were guilty. Is the Lord just and fair to us? Surely we are better than our fathers, and yet we are suffering more than they."

"You have idols in your hearts," Ezekiel told them. "When you believe that the Lord God is different from what he really is, then you have a picture in your hearts that is an idol. You are not thinking of our God who is righteous and holy.

"When you think you are suffering for the sins of your fathers, you are mistaken," Ezekiel impressed upon them. "Each man is free before the Lord to choose what he shall do. If a man had a father who did not give bread to the hungry or garments to the needy, or who took another's wife, or worshiped before idols, then that father must suffer for his sins. If the son will do what is lawful and right, if he will not oppress the helpless, if he will not profane the Sabbath, if he will not have contempt for his parents, if he will obey the commandments of the Lord, he will live. And if our nation does not obey, the Lord will yet be with those among us who do live after his laws."

The people thought about Ezekiel's words and fasted to atone for their sins. But they did not feel that their question was answered completely. They continued to ask, "Why do the righteous suffer when the wicked prosper?" Their own religion was so much better than the Babylonian religion, and yet the Babylonians were lording it over them. Ezekiel had given them part of the answer, but there seemed to be more to say. They would trust the Lord to reveal the answer to them when his time came.

They pondered and pondered over the ways of God, and a great desire to be obedient to God possessed them. "He did not choose us to be his people because of our merit, but because he loved us," they decided. "He has a right to our obedience." Then one of their leaders, who had been taught by Ezekiel, compiled and edited a book of laws. Over and again it says to the reader, "You shall be holy: for I the Lord your God am holy."

These laws gave many directions about keeping the Sabbath and the feasts. They told about food that might not be eaten and about the slaughtering of animals. All these were regulations that grew out of the people's past and were valued because they helped to keep them separate from their heathen neighbors. The laws did not let the people forget that to do justly and love mercy was most important in serving the Lord. "Thou shalt not hate thy brother in thine heart," they read, "but thou shalt love thy neighbour as thyself."

The exiles thought much about the story of their people. The more they meditated over it, the more clearly they saw how the Lord had guided them and had taught them to know him. They had carried with them into exile the records of all that had happened to them in the past. Now as they looked back they saw what

God's purpose for them had always been and where they had gone astray. So some of them began to rewrite the story in the light of their new understanding of God's ways with them. They wrote it in such a way that when the people read it they would want to live acceptably to God. "When the ancient writers lived," the exiles thought, "they did not know, as clearly as we know now, what the Lord was saying through all that was happening to them. Everyone who reads our scriptures must know that all through the years the Lord was revealing himself to us."

The years went by. The people had grown in faith and insight, but their questions were not stilled and their homesickness never left them. "Jeremiah said that we shall return to Jerusalem. It will be a long time, but we shall return. Ezekiel said that the Lord will restore our nation. But did the prophets really know?" the people wondered.

Life in Babylonia had become more difficult. Under the kings that came after Nebuchadnezzar there was great unrest in the Babylonian Empire. No one defended the exiles when they suffered oppression. They asked the same questions as of old: "If God is just, why do the wicked prosper and the righteous suffer? Has God forgotten us?"

There arose at this time a new prophet, one whose name we do not know, a man who had great compassion for his people. We do not know whether he lived in Babylonia or Palestine, but we do know that he was a prophet to the Israelites who were scattered throughout all those lands. Perhaps he sent his messages to them in letters. He was sure of the love of the Lord, not only for the people of Israel, but for all mankind. He knew more clearly than any prophet before him that the Lord God of Israel, holy and righteous, was the one all-powerful God of all the world. Years later his writings were put in the same book with those of the prophet Isaiah.

"It is not only because we have sinned that we suffer," he said. "Many of God's servants have had to suffer because of their faithfulness. They have been hated and badly treated because they refused to give up their faith in God. Whoever will be God's servant must expect to suffer. Somehow that kind of suffering will help to bring other people nearer to God. His ways are higher than our ways and his thoughts greater than our thoughts. He would not be God if we could understand his ways."

He heard the Lord saying to him: "Comfort my people. Tell them I have not cast them off. Their sins are forgiven. As a mother cannot forget her child, so I cannot forget my people. If they will but trust in me, they will receive new strength."

At first the people thought, "Those are good words, but we are suffering and there is no sign of change."

The prophet told them, "The Lord has a great and surprising plan. He has led our people through the desert once; he will again prepare the way through the wilderness."

How could that be? The people could see no inclination on the part of the Babylonian rulers to let their captives go! They did not yet know that the Babylonian Empire was losing its power. Meanwhile, the Persians under Cyrus were gaining strength, and conquering country after country. "The Lord will use Cyrus the Persian as his instrument to free you and to restore Israel," the prophet sent word to the captives in different parts of Babylonia. "You shall go forth from Babylonia, not in haste or in flight, but in honor and as a people respected. Sanctify yourselves that you may be worthy to carry back the golden vessels of the Lord's Temple. The Lord will go before you and he will protect you. It is his purpose that through you all the kingdoms of the earth will become the Kingdom of our God."

What had seemed impossible happened. The great city of Babylon fell to the Persian ruler without even a battle. The discord within it had made the city too weak to stand against an invading army.

Cyrus was a wise ruler, who believed that his empire would be strong if its people were made happy and if subject people could worship as they desired. Besides, a grateful and loyal people in Palestine would be useful in some plans he had for the future. So Cyrus issued a decree that freed the exiles to return to their homeland in Judah. He gave back to them all the golden Temple vessels that Nebuchadnezzar had carried away to Babylonia. Bearing their Temple treasure and the old and new scriptures of their people, they journeyed forth.

Many of the exiles remained behind, including not only those

who had taken on Babylonian ways, but some of the faithful servants of the Lord as well. They said: "Our children have grown up
here and are established in this country. Let them stay. It is not
as if they were learning to be untrue to the Lord. We have been
teaching them to serve him and they are keeping the law more
devotedly than we kept it in the homeland years ago." Still others
decided to let their families wait in Babylonia until new commu-
nities could be established in Judah.

The company that set forth across the desert knew that the
Lord was leading them. Rejoicing greatly that the time of captivity was over, they went out in faith that it was God's purpose to
establish his people again in the land he had given their fathers.
Surely they should trust him whom they had learned to know as
the only God. He was their God and there was none beside him.
The time would come, they believed, when all nations to the ends
of the earth would come to Jerusalem to worship him.

XII. *"I order all my life by thy behests, I hate all godless ways"* *

THE people of our story had come to be known as Jews because of the name of their tribe and country, Judah. They knew themselves to be the people of God, inheriting the promises and the task given to Israel long ago. While the great empires of East and West were contending with each other, these Jews founded a nation that became more and more a Church. It was a wonderful adventure, made possible by their faith. Although they could not have their own national government, they remained a united people.

WHEN the pilgrims arrived in Palestine from Babylonia, they found that they had to be pioneers in their own home country. In fact, only a small part of that country made them welcome. Neighboring tribes, some of them enemies of Judah from olden times, had pushed their way into Judah. Not all the people Nebuchadnezzar had left in the land were still there, for great numbers had fled into Egypt. A small and discouraged population in the

* Ps. 119: 128 (Moffatt's Translation).

84

ruins of the city of Jerusalem and in the country immediately around the city welcomed the pilgrims and helped them to build houses to shelter them against the weather. They also worshiped with them at the altar that stood amid the ruins of the Temple.

Cyrus of Persia had charged them to rebuild the Temple. They needed it, and they wanted it too, as a sign of God's presence with them, and as a place where they could worship according to the ways they had been taught.

They began to lay the foundation. Then trouble arose. Neighbors from the north came and said, "Let us help you build, for we too seek your God." But the Jews thought: "Those of the north have not learned all that we have been taught through our sorrows and through our laws and prophets. They do not know the true way to worship God. We cannot risk having them be part of us." And some among them warned: "It is only to us Cyrus gave permission to build. He might think it treason if the people of the country gather here." So the offer of help was turned down with a rebuff: "We ourselves will build the Temple to the Lord of Israel, as Cyrus, the king of Persia, has commanded us."

It was a long time, however, before the Temple was finally rebuilt. First the angry neighbors prevented the work. They said, "If you won't let us help you, we will find ways to hinder you!" And they found many ways to harass the builders. There was a new king in Persia who did not know of Cyrus' interest in the Temple. They sent a warning to him that if Jerusalem were fortified again it would perhaps become rebellious as it had been before. A letter from the king ordered the Jews to cease their building. The Jews also were hindered by their own discouragement in everything they tried to do. The lordly temples that the Babylonians had built for their gods were in their minds, and the memory of the glory of Solomon's Temple. For many years they would be too poor to build a worthy Temple, even if they had the king's permission. So they spent their time working their fields and tending their orchards and vineyards and making their houses stronger by erecting stone walls around them. But the hard work failed to bring prosperity. Drought and hail ruined their crops; raids by tribes from beyond their borders brought much violence.

Then the prophet Haggai arose and startled them into action. "Consider, men of Judah," he said, "if it is right that you perfect your own houses and leave the Lord's house in ruins. The Lord says to you: 'Go into the hill country and bring wood and build the Temple according to your means, and I will be pleased with it. I will be glorified by the faithfulness of my people.'"

Under Haggai's leadership they started with a will. When they lagged, he said: "Some of you who saw the first Temple think too little of this house we are building. The Lord God who made a covenant with our forefathers that he would guide them and care for them is still in our midst. He is shaking the nations. There will be great changes. When He who will reign in the Lord's name comes, the nations that now oppress us will bring their gifts to this Temple. Its glory will be greater than that of the former Temple. The Lord will bless you if you build the Temple."

Zechariah joined Haggai in guiding the people, and he too told them of a great future. But he knew that more was needed than a temple. "When we stop the oppression of our own brothers and show mercy and compassion to the widow, the fatherless, the stranger, then the Lord will bring comfort and prosperity." When the people were discouraged because the city walls were not restored, he promised: "The Lord will encircle the city and he will guard it. His glory will be in it against the day when he will be king of all the earth."

The walls of the Temple rose, and at last it was ready to be dedicated to the worship of God. With priests and Levites and Temple singers at their appointed places and tasks, the people brought their offering of sacrifice and praise. The very oldest people, those who had seen the former Temple in its glory, wept. But in their hearts they rejoiced with the rest that the Lord, whom they thought of as far above them reigning over the nations, now also had his abode near to them, in his Temple.

Time went on. The glowing promises of the prophets were not fulfilled. Having a temple with regular services did not make the country prosperous and good. Some merchants and traders had opened places of business, but few people came back from far lands to join the small company in Jerusalem. It was known far and wide that the walls were still in ruins and could offer no protection against the many treacherous foes. As poverty and oppression and danger and lawlessness continued, some of the inhabitants began to mock the faithful servants of God, saying: "One is no better off for serving God! God is not in this city. Would he leave the walls in ruins if he were?"

The faithful themselves, believing their sins were the cause of their troubles, prayed earnestly:

"Create a clean heart in us, O God. Do good to our city and build the walls of Jerusalem."

The years passed. One generation died and another took its place, but conditions did not change. Then one day word went around: "The king's cupbearer has come from Shushan in Persia, one of the king's most trusted officers! Nehemiah is here, one of our own people!"

"What will his coming mean?" everybody wondered. They had not long to wait before they learned. Nehemiah called a meeting of the leaders. No one knew how carefully he had studied the situation of the city and its inhabitants in the three days he had been there. Quietly, during the night, he had made a journey all around its walls to examine the ruins.

First he told the assembled leaders his story: "You wonder how I came here and by what right I ask you to meet with me. It was in answer to prayer that it came about. Some men of Judah came to Shushan and they told of the affliction of Jerusalem, that its walls were still broken down. I mourned and fasted and I prayed to God day and night. I asked that God would soften the heart of the king so that he would let me go for a time to the city of my fathers, for I am the king's cupbearer. It happened one day when I brought wine to the king that he asked the reason for my sadness, and I told him that the city of my fathers was still in ruins. Then, because the blessing of God was upon me, the king gave me leave to come and build the city. He has given me letters to his governors that they permit the work, and a letter to the keeper of the king's forests that he grant the wood that is needed." Then Nehemiah told them the plans he had made as to the way the work could be done. With one voice the leaders said, "Let us arise and build."

Soon the walls began to rise, for the people worked gladly.

Every family and all the workmen's guilds knew just what they must do, and they did it.

Then the enemies learned what was going on and organized for an attack. "What are these feeble Jews doing?" they mocked. "Will they make walls out of heaps of burned rubbish?" Nehemiah, hearing this, said, "We will make our prayers to God and set a watch against these enemies day and night." Half the people stood fully armed guarding the walls, and the other half worked with swords girded on them. A trumpeter stayed beside Nehemiah to give the alarm if it should be needed. Those who lived outside the walls came within for safety during the night.

The work progressed, but Nehemiah learned that all was not well among the workers. Some living on farms outside the walls were greatly disturbed about their children who were in slavery. Their anger was great against those whom they blamed for their trouble. "Because of a famine," they explained, "and enemy raiders and heavy taxes paid to the Persian government, we had to mortgage our farms. Our sons and daughters became bond servants that our families might have food to eat. Now we cannot redeem our children because our fields and houses are held by the wealthy men of Jerusalem."

"Those men of property are our brothers," these fathers said. "We need food to live as they do; we love our children as they love theirs."

Nehemiah called an assembly of the nobles and the other men of wealth and reproved them. "It is not good," he told them, "it is not to the honor of our God, that the heathen should see the children of our brothers sold in slavery. My servants and I also have more money and corn than we need. We too might ask interest on loans to the poor. Let us all agree that henceforth we will make no profit from the needs of our poorer brothers. I beg of you that you restore to them the vineyards and olive orchards, the fields and houses, that were theirs, together with a part of the money and the harvest that you have taken from them."

The rich men of Jerusalem were ashamed and they said, "We will do as you say." Then Nehemiah called the priests and had the assembled men take an oath that they would keep the promise.

The work on the walls went forward with new zest, so that the enemies began to be worried over its progress. At various times they plotted how they might get Nehemiah into their hands. One day they sent word that he must come to them outside the walls to discuss something important. But he sent answer, "I am doing a great work, and I cannot come down."

On the fifty-second day of the work the walls were completed. All the city prepared for a festival. A joyful procession of the citizens around the top of the wall, to the music of cymbals and psalteries and harps, began the celebration. Then everyone went to the Temple courts, where the children joined their parents in hymns of praise that were heard over the countryside, and the priests offered sacrifices of thanksgiving.

Nehemiah was happy. He said, "Even the enemy knows that our God is with us." It became known in other countries that the city was now safe. Nehemiah had established daily services in the Temple and better government. Soon families that had fled from Judah began to return. Nehemiah's leave was up and he had to return to his work in Persia. But before he left, he guided the citizens in making laws that denied citizenship to non-Jews and forbade marriage with them. The community was still weak, and he feared that laxity in admitting heathen to it might lead again to worship of heathen gods, and that Jerusalem might lose its right to exist as the city of God. Then he returned to Shushan, the capital of the Persian Empire, but he was so uneasy in his mind about the welfare of Judah that after some twelve years he came back.

"What is this I hear? Can I believe my ears?" Nehemiah stopped to listen to some children chattering in the streets of the city to make sure that they were indeed speaking with foreign accents. It was obvious that they had fathers or mothers from Ashdod or Moab or Ammon. This meant that the laws against marriage with neighbor peoples had been broken and that the way was being opened for heathen religions to come into Judah. Nehemiah was deeply grieved, and angry too. He called an assembly and had the people swear that they would not let their sons or daughters marry outside their own people. "Remember the history of our people," he begged them, "and how much trouble has come from temptation to heathen worship. It must not happen again that our religion shall be defiled."

Some persons in the city worked on the Sabbath Day. Nehemiah reminded them of all that the Sabbath had meant to their people. "How can you forget all that happened to our fathers when they profaned the Sabbath and forgot the other laws of the Lord?" He saw trading done on the Sabbath and he sent orders, "Have the gates of the city locked on the eve of the Sabbath and do not let them be opened until the day is over." Some fish merchants from Tyre and other traders clamored for entrance in vain. They camped outside the gates and traded there until the Sabbath was over, but when the next Sabbath came Nehemiah sent them away. So they decided it was better business to come on a different day.

All the while the returned captives and their children were building a new community in Judah, other Jews still deeply interested in the religion of their fathers were growing up in Babylonia, in Persia, and in Egypt. They thought about their past and prayed that Jerusalem might become a worthy dwelling of the Lord. They wrote detailed directions for obeying the law they had inherited and regulations about the kind of Temple worship they thought worthy of the Lord.

Among those in Persia was Ezra, who had his heart set upon obeying the law and teaching it to his people. More than seventeen hundred of his fellow Jews gathered about him and with the king's permission they journeyed to Jerusalem. Great was the joy in Jerusalem when the caravan arrived, bearing golden vessels for the Temple and freewill offerings and many costly gifts from those who remained behind.

Ezra let it be known that the greatest gift the caravan had carried was a Book of the Law, and the people begged that he read it to them. A pulpit was erected in an open space in the city. All the children old enough to understand gathered with their parents to hear the reading. The children could understand the words they heard, but they did not know why their parents should be weeping when they heard these laws set forth. "It is because we see how far we have again fallen short of the expectations of the Lord," the parents explained.

Then Ezra came to a happy place in the book. It was about the festivals, giving directions how they should be celebrated. All the nations had harvest festivals. "The people of Israel shall celebrate theirs by living in booths of green branches," Ezra read, "as a memorial of the time when their forefathers lived in booths in the wilderness and God led them to this land."

When Ezra read the directions for the thanksgiving festival as a feast of booths, the people were filled with gladness. This festival had not been celebrated since the days of Joshua. It was the time of year for this harvest festival, and the people went into the country to gather boughs. For seven days they lived in the green booths they erected on the roofs and in the courtyards, and every day they listened to Ezra as he read sections of the law and taught its meaning. One day the reading was about the Sabbath and acceptable sacrifices, and about festivals and the day of atonement. Another day it was about the Temple tax to support the priests and the Levites, the singers and doorkeepers of the Temple. Again they heard about confessing wrongs that were done and about making them right, and about justice in the courts and the care of the poor. He taught them once more the laws forbidding intermarriage with foreigners, and read provisions for the teaching of the law at regular times.

At the end of the reading an assembly was held so that the people might decide what they intended to do about the law. Ezra reminded the people of all God had done for them, in choosing them for his people, in leading them out of Egypt, in giving them Moses for a leader and lawgiver. He led the congregation in prayer, confessing how in times past they had not obeyed God's law, and acknowledging that they still deserved punishment. "If you should be angry with us now," Ezra prayed, "there would be no remnant left, for you are righteous and just." The representatives of the people went forward, one after the other, and put their seals to the lawbook as a sign that it should be the law of the people.

The law not to intermarry was hard to enforce because even in the families of some of the priests and other leaders there had been intermarriage with foreigners. The law provided that in such case the wife or husband who was not a Jew must be given

up. This caused great hardship to many, but the law was en-
forced, and those who would not comply went to Samaria to live.

Under the overlordship of Persia there had come into being in
Judah a nation whose life was centered in its worship. All the
people's festivals had become religious festivals, all their laws
were religious laws, for no matter what these laws demanded,
obedience to them was considered part of the worship of God.
Nehemiah and Ezra and the faithful among the people hoped
that now there would come into being a holy community in
which everyone would know that life and death depended upon
obedience to the law of God.

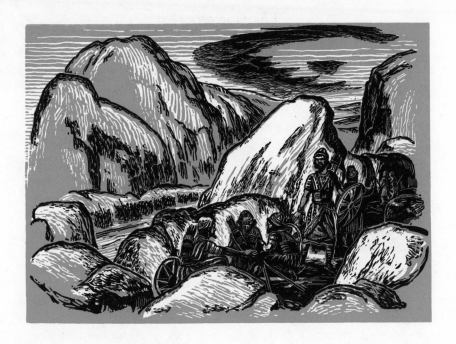

XIII. *"Though he slay me, yet will I trust in him"*

OUR Bible does not tell what happened during more than four centuries after the time of Nehemiah and Ezra. There are books in the Bible, however, that reflect the experiences of the people and tell what they were thinking during most of this period. They were living under foreign rulers and in the midst of warring empires. Their small nation was kept alive and united through their faith in God and their belief that he would use Israel to make righteousness triumph on earth. There were no prophets in these centuries, but God was not without witnesses.

EACH shall live under his own vine and fig tree," the prophet of old had promised. There would come a time when no one would make Israel afraid any more. When foreign conquerors marched through the land, that day seemed very far away. But when there came years of peace, the faithful wondered, "Has the promised time finally come?" Perhaps peace had come because the people were worshiping the Lord God and him only, and no one thought of Baal worship any more. The God they worshiped was the one true God—Israel had learned that and could never forget it. But could they be righteous enough to please God, so that he would keep on blessing them?

Whether near or far away, the faithful in Israel were united in worship each morning and evening through the burnt offering on the altar in the great inner court of the Temple in Jerusalem. It consisted of a lamb, offered with the addition of flour and a libation of wine. Each morning the ritual began before dawn, when in the flickering light of the ever-burning altar fire a solitary priest approached with implements of gold to remove the ashes accumulated during the night. As the Levites chanted psalms, other priests took their turn in trimming the lamps, dividing the sacrificial victim, placing it upon the stone grid which covered the sea of fire upon the altar, offering finally the prescribed prayers and benedictions.

Although to many Jews these sacrifices were mere form, the faithful thought of them as gifts to God. At the time of the offering they read in their homes the psalms of penitence and thanksgiving which reminded them of both the justice and the loving-kindness of God.

On the Sabbath, and at festivals, there were more elaborate services, with priests constantly encircling the altar of sacrifice. All through the week private offerings were brought in fulfillment of vows or in repentance for sins. Often the worshipers had traveled far to Jerusalem.

Priests and Levites and Temple servants saw to it that every rule regarding Temple worship was obeyed with care. They said, "It is better to do more than God requires than to do too little, for God has made us his people and deserves our gratitude." Therefore the wood for the sacrifice was sorted piece by piece so that there might be none with wormholes; all the fruits were carefully selected so that none marred by stain would be included in the offerings. When a priest had a temporary blemish on his body, he did not serve in the Temple until it was healed. In making their worship correct according to all the priestly rules, many in Israel forgot all about the prophets' teachings. But there were always some who remembered that without repentance no sacrifice avails before God. They read their psalms of penitence and prayed, "Create in me a clean heart, O God; and renew a right spirit within me."

"We must never again bring God's wrath upon us by disobeying his law," all the people agreed. So they built synagogues all over the land where the men and women and children might learn the law. The law was the delight of the faithful. They enjoyed reciting in the synagogue the words from one of the psalms: "O how I love thy law! It is my meditation all the day. I will keep the commandments of my God."

Large groups of men known as scribes spent all their time studying the law and explaining it to the people. Many regulations had been added to the older lawbooks and the people were taught to observe them with care. There were rules providing for times of prayer, for fasts, for ritual washings, and for the keeping of the Sabbath. As time went on, the scribes gathered all the sacred books together and saw to it that the books of law and history and prophecy, and the psalms and the sayings of the wise, were preserved and honored. Wherever they lived in various parts of the world, worshipers of the God of Israel were recognized by the way they kept the Sabbath and were respected as decent and honorable people.

Many people came from distant lands to live in Palestine. There were those who had fled in time of persecution, those who had stayed on in lands to which long ago they had been exiled, and sometimes people of other nations who had accepted Judaism as their religion. Great was the rejoicing. "A nation born in a day! Who has heard such a thing? Who has seen such a thing?" wrote one of Israel's preachers. A poet expressed his joy in a psalm:

> "When the Lord brought back those that returned to Zion
>   we were like those that dreamed.
> The Lord has done great things for us,
>   whereof we are glad."

Was the day coming of which the prophet Zechariah had spoken? He had said, "Many people and strong nations shall come to seek the Lord of hosts in Jerusalem and to entreat the favor of the

Lord." It seemed already to be the day of which he prophesied, "Ten will take hold of the skirt of a Jew and say, We will worship with you, for we have heard that God is with you."

The Jews had been taught that they were called of God to be "a light to lighten the gentiles." God had revealed himself to them so that they might share their knowledge of him with all men. They were so sure, however, that the God of all the world was their God in a very special sense that they often forgot his concern for all mankind. In times of great suffering the Jews felt that God must hate the nations that oppressed them as much as they themselves did.

"We were meant to share our knowledge of God," said one of their thoughtful men, "and we cannot share anything to which we are holding so tightly!" He planned how he might help his people to understand God's purpose for them, and to realize that they must do much more than guard their religion from contamination. "To be sure," he said to himself, "the people of Judah were a long time learning to have nothing to do with idols, and during that long time it was well that they kept themselves apart from people who served idols. But now they must learn to share their religion. That is why they were taught to know God!"

Thinking of many of the Jews he knew, he wrote a story about a prophet named Jonah. In the story Jonah was asked by the Lord to go to Nineveh, capital city of Israel's long-time enemy Assyria, and tell the people of Nineveh to repent. But Jonah rebelled. He did not want the people of Nineveh to repent and live. "Because of all their cruelties to God's people they deserve only to die," he argued. So he took ship and sailed in the opposite direction. A storm arose in which Jonah was cast into the sea and was swallowed by a big fish which God had prepared. The writer intended his people to see that in their attitude to other nations they had been like Jonah. Jonah's troubles were meant to remind them of the captivity and other misfortunes that they had suffered because of their disobedience to God. In the belly of the fish Jonah repented and was thrown on dry land. But he had repented only after a fashion, not thoroughly, and in this too, Jonah was like the people of Judah.

At last Jonah went to Nineveh and preached repentance to the people there. But he did not expect any good to come of it. When the people repented and turned to God and were not punished as he had told them they would be, he became angry and depressed. Why should this enemy know God's mercy? God should have sent judgment upon these heathen! The writer knew that this was what most Jews wanted to happen to all foreign nations.

While Jonah was sorrowing over what had happened, a plant grew up which sheltered him from the hot sun. Soon, however, a worm gnawed at the stalk of the plant so that it died. Jonah was still more disgruntled and said, "It is better for me to die than to live." Then God spoke sternly to Jonah: "You mourn for a gourd vine for which you have done nothing that it should grow. Should not I care about the one hundred and twenty thousand men, women, and children of Nineveh, and their cattle, and spare them from destruction?"

Some of those who read the book became very thoughtful. They said: "We are as bad and selfish as Jonah! Perhaps we must revise some of our laws! Perhaps our laws are not all the Lord's will! Perhaps at one time it was his will that we should bar non-Jews from companionship with us, but not any more! He wants us to love mercy and to have compassion and to share our knowledge of God." There were others, however, who made answer: "How could we be a people at all if we had not observed the law that separates us from all other nations? We should now have lost ourselves among the nations of the world, and should be worshiping as they do. What about our brothers, the people of the Northern Kingdom, who went into captivity? Did they not become part of the nations where they settled? Could we have kept the Lord's covenant at all if we had let the Baal worshipers, and the sun and star worshipers, mingle freely with us? There are still heathen about us. We might become like them!"

"Perhaps they will think differently about this if I tell them a story of olden times," said another man to himself. So he wrote a love story to prove his point. It was about a young girl in the ancient days named Ruth, whose home was in Moab and who married an Israelite. She became so great a blessing to her family that the neighbors said to Naomi, her Israelite mother-in-law, "Your daughter-in-law who loves you is better than seven sons to you." And yet she was not a Jewess, but a woman of Moab! The writer knew that many would say, "But that was long ago, before we had our law!" So he told them in the story: "She was the ancestress of our greatest king, David, whose successor we are always awaiting! She brought great blessing to our people! Perhaps by our law that shuts out foreigners we are keeping much blessing from ourselves!"

There came a time when the faith and loyalty of the Jews were tested to the uttermost. It was well that they had learned to guard their religion. Peace had lasted until the latter years of the Persian Empire. But when a cruel, capricious ruler named Artaxerxes Ochus came to the throne, there was trouble. Various parts of the empire rebelled against him, and the Jews became involved in the general unrest. By the revenge that Artaxerxes Ochus took, hundreds lost their lives.

"Why should this happen to us? We have been obeying the law as well as we know!" mourned some who had prided themselves upon the strict observance of the law. "It is not possible for anyone to be good enough in the judgment of the righteous, holy God," others answered, and they prayed: "We shall always deserve punishment, but you are our Father. Do not remember our iniquity." Still others prayed for vengeance, saying: "They who have reproached us have reproached our God. Render sevenfold return, O God, upon those who have defied you!"

Many who were puzzled to know why even the righteous should suffer took comfort when they read the drama of Job. It told the story of a man of strong faith who suffered great disasters, losing his family, his possessions, and his health. But he refused to give up his humble faith in God. The writer had Job say: "I believed in God when I was still happy, before all my troubles came. I will still believe, even though I cannot understand the reason for my troubles." The people read this book, and then, like Job, they looked at the stars and the sea and, overcome by the mystery of God's creation, they found peace. They could say: "We will be silent in the presence of God and trust his wisdom and his justice. However mysterious his rule is, we know that he is righteous!"

Philip of Macedon left to his son Alexander the empire he had been building in the West. Then Alexander brought his armies east against the Persians and defeated them. Their dominions, including Palestine, became a part of Alexander's new world empire. Upon Alexander's death the empire was divided among his generals. Ptolemy of Egypt ruled over Palestine at first. Eventually it came under the rule of Syria. During these years of Greek rule and influence, some cities in Palestine became altogether Greek in population and government. In others that were still Jewish, Greek customs took hold. In Jerusalem the aristocratic priestly party, known later as the Sadducees, appreciated Greek culture very much. They liked to please their rulers, who were interested in spreading the ways of the Greeks through all of the new empires.

When Antiochus Epiphanes of Syria became ruler, the Greek party among the Jews upheld him in his endeavor to stamp out the Jewish religion. Great sorrows came upon the faithful. The trouble came to a head when Antiochus, who always needed money, was bribed to appoint as high priest one who, according to the law of Moses, was not eligible for the position. To Antiochus a high priest in Jerusalem was merely another local governor in one of the districts of the empire. When the faithful Jews refused to accept the appointment, Antiochus considered their act rebellion. To his mind it was out of the question that he could let this small people claim their law to be a higher authority than his will. The Greek party among the Jews aided and abetted him when he undertook to root out the Jewish religion.

The faithful in the country, seeing how great was the danger to their religion, organized to defend it at all costs. This band, probably the forerunners of the Pharisees, cared fiercely for the faith and aimed to preserve the law and the traditions at risk of their lives.

Antiochus was ruthless. All copies of the law which his men could find were destroyed. He made it a capital offense to read the scriptures or observe the Sabbath. An altar to Zeus was erected in the Temple. Many of the faithful were slain or burned to death, being captured while keeping the Sabbath or at their daily devotions.

To avoid death or the slave market, some Jews fled to Egypt;

many lived hidden in caves and deserted regions. Never had their faith been tested more severely. Then word was whispered about a book full of comfort. "Have you read it yet? Have you heard about the stories in the book of Daniel?" It was circulated secretly, this book of hope and consolation, which was named "Daniel" after its chief character. The stories in it assured the reader that the rise and fall of the great empires and all that had happened to the Jewish people was part of God's plan. Nothing could defeat his purpose. Righteousness would triumph in the end, and God would establish his Kingdom of justice and truth under his own Anointed One. The book told of Daniel, a hero persecuted for his faith during the days of the nation's captivity. Daniel had not been hurt even in a den of lions, and his friends came unharmed out of a fiery furnace of tribulation, heated seven times hotter than ever before. "God is with us in all our trials," it meant to say; "we are never out of his care."

The book contained also the story of an irresponsible Babylonian king. At a riotous banquet a mysterious hand appeared, writing on the wall the words, "Mene, mene, tekel, upharsin"— words of judgment which meant in part, "You have been weighed and found wanting." That night, the king Belshazzar lost his life and throne. When the people read this story, it assured them: "Tyrants cannot prevail against the purposes and the judgment of God. He will not let Antiochus defeat his plan for his people. God's servants will not be forsaken."

As the Syrians went forward with their plan to root out the religion of the Jews, the king's emissary came to a town in the hills of Judah that was the home of the old priest Mattathias. He asked the priest to offer sacrifice upon a heathen altar. Mattathias refused and slew the king's representative, sending out word to the people, "Whoever is jealous for the law, and maintains the covenant with God, let him come after me!"

Many came to join him and his sons. "It does not matter whether we are one or many if we are in the right!" was their slogan. Mattathias turned over to his sons the leadership of the people who had gathered about him. These men gave good generalship to their followers, and the hilly country favored guerrilla warfare. Before long they had gained sufficient strength to free

Jerusalem from the Greek party and to re-establish Temple worship. Antiochus' strength was waning and he gave less and less resistance to the Maccabeans. (This was the name by which all the sons of Mattathias came to be known, after Judas Maccabeus, the most notable among them.) Eventually they were powerful enough to unite the people and to establish an independent nation.

After Antiochus' death several rivals claimed his throne. His empire disintegrated, while Rome became the new world power. The Maccabeans were able to hold power in Palestine for a time, on the basis of a friendly treaty with Rome.

Because a Jewish state had been established, some in Israel rejoiced, "The promised rule of God has come!" But their joy did not last, for the Maccabean rule was worldly. The Pharisees were outraged that a warrior, Simon Maccabeus, had made himself high priest as well as king. They were in continual strife with the Sadducees, the high priest's party. Presently, struggle between rivals for the place of high priest started civil war. When a Roman general was asked to settle the dispute, he came in to make peace—and also to take power. Now the Jews were under the authority of a Roman.

Rome had no rivals—she ruled the world. Would her overpowering might absorb the small Jewish nation and its religion? The people prayed it might not be so. They read over and over again the prophecies in their scriptures that told of the Messiah who would come to bring God's own rule.

Some took comfort in the hope for a warrior king, whom they believed God would raise from among them to give him power over Rome. Others read expectantly the prophecy in the book of Daniel concerning one who would come from on high, on the clouds of heaven, to establish through the power of God an everlasting Kingdom that would never be destroyed.

The people clung more than ever to all that made them different from other peoples: to the Temple, to their law—to the keeping of the Sabbath, their food laws, their ritual cleansing, their exclusion of non-Jews from companionship. They could not imagine God's purposes' being fulfilled through his people except by way of their law, their Temple worship, their nation. If they remained faithful to their law and their worship, God would use Israel for his glory and would bring glory to Israel in his own good time. Through his people, they were confident, he would establish a Kingdom where "all people and nations and languages" would serve him.

The One Story

PART TWO

I. *"The beginning of the gospel of Jesus Christ"*

OUR story has carried us to the New Testament. New Testament means "new covenant," and a covenant is a promise. The promise that God made to his people in the Old Testament was fulfilled in the New. The prophet Jeremiah looked forward to this time when he said the Lord would make a new covenant with his people, writing his law in their hearts, that all men might come to know him.

COUNTLESS prayers went up to God from the people among the hills and valleys, in the villages and towns of Palestine: "Lord God of Israel, visit and redeem your people. All our hope is in you! Let us see your salvation!"

On the surface there seemed no cause for the unhappiness of so great a part of the population. After long years of turmoil, the Romans had conquered all the warring nations and there was peace in the world at last.

But there was a deep longing for change, a great hope for a different future, and an expectation that God's rule on earth, which would make all things new, must begin soon. When the people prayed for redemption and salvation, and for a change from present conditions, however, there was no agreement in their minds about the way in which it would come or what it would be like when it came.

The party known as the Zealots, regarded as traitors by the Romans, worked hard for converts. They prayed to the Lord for salvation, but they were not waiting for him to bring about the desired freedom from Rome. Too baffled and angry to wait, they were preparing to take a strong hand themselves in the process of redemption, which for them meant national independence. They would not accept the fact that no forces they might be able to muster could prevail against this vast empire that was ruling the world. They plotted to overthrow the Roman power.

"God is our ruler and he alone!" the Zealots said, and their motto was, "No tribute to Caesar." Their heroes were the men who had been executed by Herod for taking down from over the Temple gate the great golden eagle, emblem of Rome; so also was Judas the Galilean, who with his followers had been killed in a rebellion against Rome. They wanted a Messiah, an Anointed One, a ruler whom God himself would send. They expected him to come with a sword in his hand to avenge their people and to bring judgment upon the rulers they hated. "God will send a new king of David's line who will conquer Rome and raise Israel to power," they proclaimed, and they believed it firmly. Were they not God's people? How, then, could they remain subject to unbelievers?

Their trust in God was great. They took for granted it was his will that they should die rather than live under the rule of a heathen power. These men saw that the high priest, with others of the hereditary priesthood, and the whole party of the Sadducees were influenced by Roman ways. They saw clearly the danger to their religion.

Attendance at festivals in Jerusalem brought them no joy. "A day in thy courts is better than a thousand," their forefathers had sung. The Levites sang that same psalm now in the magnificent Temple with its crowded courts. But the Zealots' worship was poisoned by the knowledge that the Temple had been built by a king they despised. He loved Rome more than Israel. Herod had built the house of God in an endeavor to appease his Jewish subjects. The Zealots had no patience with the rank and file of the people, who could see no danger in this foreign influence. All around them the Romans were building theaters, fortresses, gymnasiums, palaces, and baths. Many of the people rather liked all this activity because it brought them more business and income. "They are traitors to Israel who work for the Romans," the Zealots protested.

It was small wonder that many Jews accepted jobs wherever there was opportunity to earn a living. "What shall we eat?" "How shall we clothe our children?" These were vexing and anxious questions. The tribute levied by Rome, added to the Temple tax and tithes and other offerings every Jew was expected to pay, was an almost unbearable burden to all but the well-to-do. If the people complained, the Romans would say: "We are not asking more tax from you than from others of our subject nations. They are grateful to us for keeping the peace, for building roads and bridges." When the Jews rejoined, "But unlike other nations, we have also a Temple tax to pay," the answer would come: "That is not our concern. Speak to your religious leaders." When the people appealed to the high priest and his party in Jerusalem, they found no help from them either. The Temple leaders had little concern for the needy and the troubled of heart whom God expected them to serve. Their care was for the Temple system, through which they gained wealth and influence. The curt answer of the Jewish leaders was, "It is your duty to God to pay the Temple tax and the tithes, and to bring the sacrifices the law directs."

It was not only the double tax and the unjust increases often demanded by dishonest collectors of the Roman tax that caused poverty; there was also the unfair competition of slave labor. Small landowners and businessmen were unable to purchase slaves to assist in vineyard or farm or garden or shop, so they were driven out of business because they could not sell products at the same prices as the rich owners of slaves. Then those whom they had employed lost their jobs and had to stand all day long in the market place hoping, often in vain, that someone might hire them. They had no reserves for times of drought or sickness or unemployment; for many of these people salvation meant a time of prosperity and plenty. When they prayed, "Send us thy salvation," they were thinking of freedom from daily cares. God's rule to them meant a time when there would be no anxieties about tomorrow's bread.

The Pharisees and scribes, the accepted leaders of the people, were impatient at the frenzy of the Zealots, who only caused trouble with Rome. Like the Zealots, however, they confidently expected God's judgment upon Rome and the triumph of Israel. It would come, many of them thought, through a great act of power from on high. The Pharisees and scribes said: "What we need to do is to keep the law. Leave all else to God. If we keep the law, God will deliver us." So they prayed and fasted as often as the law required, and oftener. They urged continually upon the people the washings and fastings and offerings that were prescribed by the law. Saying so many prayers, they thought, would surely hasten the coming of the day of salvation, a day of glory for Israel.

Scattered among the citizens of town and city, or living quietly in the hills and on the farms, were those whose first concern was the will of God—they were the saving remnant. These quiet, faithful ones obeyed the law as well as they could. They regretted that there were not enough hours in the day to do honor to all the laws that were important to the Pharisees and scribes. "If just for one day all the laws were obeyed," some of the scribes said, "the Lord would send his Anointed." So the faithful went to the synagogues and to the Temple. They read the Law and the Prophets. They prayed and brought the sacrifices the law demanded. But they did not find great joy in these activities, for they feared that, in spite of all they had done, they would not be found good enough.

They were comforted when they read the psalms and were reminded of God's mercy. They prayed, "Have mercy upon us, O God, according to your loving-kindness: according unto the multitude of your tender mercies blot out our transgressions." Surely he would not let their people and the faith they had so long cherished be overcome by the might of the world! Surely he would soon send them a prophet who would show the way out of the present confusion!—someone who would tell them what God was saying to them through the things that were happening, who understood the signs of the times, and who knew God's will.

They did not know how God would send salvation to them, how a savior would come, but they knew God would not forget them. Was the Messiah, by any possibility, even now among them although unrecognized, they wondered? If so, when would he declare himself?

The whole country was stirring as the word went round: "There is a prophet by the Jordan baptizing. He wears a hairy mantle with a leather girdle, like the prophets of old. Maybe it is Elijah come back! He says that the Messiah, the Coming One, is soon to be here, that we must get ready for the Kingdom of God which the Messiah will usher in."

They came from far and near to hear John, who had become known as "the baptizer." He baptized in the Jordan those who accepted his message of repentance, and this was a sign to them of the cleansing of their lives. The people came in crowds, although he had no pleasant words for them. "Here is one who cares about important things," they said, as they remembered the prophets' teachings. John's message, "The Kingdom is soon to come," was welcomed even by the thoughtless, who looked for a kingdom to bring Israel glory. John did not let them stay thoughtless. "He sounds like Amos," they said, and indeed he did—for John too proclaimed: "The Lord will establish his rule on earth, but judgment will come first. Change your sinful ways and turn to him. God will destroy the wicked, for it is only then that the day of salvation can come. It is God's harvesttime, and he will do with us as the farmer does with his winnowing fan. The chaff will be separated from the grain and will be burned!"

John used other parables of harvesttime to tell his message. He remembered how snakes and other vermin hastened to escape the flames of burning stubble in the harvest fields. Some of the leaders in Jerusalem lived unrighteous lives although outwardly they conformed to the law. To these hypocrites he said, "Who has told you offspring of vipers that you would escape from the wrath that is to come?" The other listeners thought, "If he is so hard on our leaders, what will he say to us?" In fear they asked, "What must we do to be saved?" There must be a change of heart, he told them, so that they would act righteously each in his own walk of life. All of them must have compassion upon the needy. "Whoever has two coats," he said, "let him give one to him who has none, and whoever has more food than he needs, let him also share." Some tax collectors whose hearts had been touched by John's message asked, "What must we do?" To them he said, "Do not charge more taxes than the fixed rate." The soldiers he admonished, "Do not loot or extort, but be content with the wages you receive."

"You all expect the Kingdom to come, and you think it will come because you are God's chosen people. It cannot come to you as you are now. As the unfruitful tree is chopped down and is not saved from the fire, so Israel, unless it repents and reforms, will not be saved."

Many of the people said, "He is a prophet; he is Elijah come back," but some said in their hearts, "Could he himself possibly be the Messiah, the Saviour who is to come?" John, sensing the question, said to them: "I baptize you only with water, as a sign of cleansing against the new day, but when he appears who is mightier than I, the Coming One, the Messiah, he will baptize you with fire. I am not worthy to untie the strings of his sandals. He will bring salvation to those who deserve it and never-ending punishment to the wicked. I am but his messenger, a voice ahead of him to prepare his way."

In one of the quiet homes in Galilee there had been growing up to manhood one who was indeed greater than John. He was soon to be known far and wide in the country as Jesus of Nazareth. He was among those who came to hear John, and he too came forward to be baptized. John recognized in Jesus one in whom God's Spirit dwelt in special measure, and he said, "You should baptize me rather than I you." But Jesus insisted that John should baptize him, for he was one with those who were willing that through them God should begin to bring in his new day.

It was when Jesus came up from the water that God filled his spirit in overflowing measure with love and compassion and power, and God gave him assurance that he was to be his long-heralded representative who would bring in the Kingdom. "You are my beloved Son," God said to him, "in whom I am well pleased."

Here was the task that he had long foreseen as his own. Just what did it mean? How was he to perform it? Jesus went straight into the wilderness and stayed for many days to think and pray over the charge God had given him. He had been sent of God, he knew, to be the Saviour his people needed. But he must be a different kind of savior than any of them expected, a messiah quite other than they had had in mind. When thoughts came to him in the desert of bringing salvation to his people by any of the ways they were expecting, he knew it was Satan and not God who was putting the ideas before him.

God had chosen him as the Coming One, the One to bring God's rule into the world. When it was clear to Jesus how God wanted him to do it, he began his work in the city that had become his home, Capernaum by the Sea of Galilee.

II. *"Thy kingdom come. Thy will be done"*

MANY in Israel expected salvation through a messiah, an anointed one, whom God would send to rule an earthly kingdom. This messiah would bring glory to Israel, destroying evil and establishing righteousness with irresistible power. What God did was so different from the people's expectation that at first it was not recognized to be as revolutionary and life-changing as it really was.

IN THE noisy cobbled streets and along the busy water front of the lakeside city of Capernaum, Jesus soon became a familiar figure to the citizens. He talked with little knots of people in the busy bazaar and on rooftops and in fishing boats while his fishermen friends were mending their nets. Before long, grown-ups and children gathered whenever they saw him come. What he said came as a shock, a pleasant shock, which made people think and feel more deeply about the things they suspected mattered most, although they had not given great attention to such things before. "Never man spoke so! And surely God is with him!" the listeners said to one another. They told their neighbors and friends of the gracious words they had heard. The compassion that flowed from Jesus to the weary and troubled made them look forward to the next time when they might be near him.

"You are looking for God's rule on earth, for his Kingdom. It is here. It is in your midst. Repent and become a part of it. You cannot point out the Kingdom, saying, 'Here it is,' or, 'There it is,' for the Kingdom of God is within you."

It was a very surprising idea to those expecting a miracle of God to bring judgment on evil and victory to righteousness. They did not understand it, but his words, ringing with great truth, compelled them to listen further.

Some were too much worried with family cares to listen, but Jesus awakened their interest by his understanding of their anxieties: "The gentiles who do not know God may ask, 'What shall we eat, what shall we drink, what shall we wear?' But with you it should be different. Seek first the Kingdom of God and its righteousness, and leave all else to God. Will he who feeds the sparrows not feed you?"

"Seek first the Kingdom"! It was plain to Jesus that his task was not simple, and he needed to gather about him a few who would learn to understand more deeply than the crowds what seeking the Kingdom meant. He needed men who would help him bring in the Kingdom. His fishermen friends came to mind, the brothers Andrew and Simon, whom he had known when he was with John the Baptizer. They were among those praying for the salvation of Israel. They were the kind of men he wanted.

These fishermen and their families were aware that the Spirit of God was strong in Jesus and that love for people flowed from him. One day when Simon's wife's mother was ill, he had taken her by the hand and raised her up, and she had served them that very evening. Their friends James and John, the sons of Zebedee, were kindred spirits. Here were four men Jesus could trust, so one day he set out to find them at the lakeside. As he walked along, people recognized him and joined themselves to him until a crowd, expecting that he would teach them, had gathered.

When he arrived at the lakeside, Jesus asked the use of Simon's fishing boat as a pulpit from which he might speak to the people. Entering the boat, he noticed signs that Simon and Andrew's catch had not been good the night before. He talked to the people and answered their questions, and when at last he had dismissed them, Jesus gave Simon some unusual directions. "Take the boat toward the center of the lake," he said, "for a catch of fish." The center when we found no fish in the likely places? That must have been Simon's first doubting thought, but he said, "We have toiled all night long and caught no fish, but at your word we will let our nets down where you say." Their catch was so great that the nets were breaking, and Simon and Andrew had to call for the help of James and John, who were in another boat. To their amazement, they filled both boats with fish. Simon, quick in action and speech, fell down before Jesus and said: "You must go away from me. I am not worthy of your friendship." But Jesus encouraged him: "Don't be afraid. I will make you a fisher of men. I will depend upon you." Jesus beckoned to James and John in the other boat to draw near, and he said to all four, Andrew and Simon and James and John, "Come with me and I will make you fishers of men."

Just what the call and the promise meant, they did not know, but as they brought their boats to land, they were resolved that whatever Jesus asked of them they would do. They accompanied him wherever he went and soon remarked to one another, "He is a fisher of men through his great compassion!" How different was their teacher from those scribes who thought they would be made unclean by contact with people ignorant of the law! Jesus took the four to places where the outcasts of the city could be found. They saw him make friends with those whose minds were tormented, those called demoniacs because their illness was thought to be caused by demons. "His life is as his teaching," they commented when they heard him say: "Blessed are the merciful, the pure in heart, the peacemakers. They shall be called sons of God. Theirs shall be the joy of the Kingdom."

As Jesus' fame spread through all Galilee, the rulers of the synagogues invited him to explain the scriptures on the Sabbath. It was their custom to ask anyone whom they considered able. Peter and Andrew and James and John saw everywhere the people's eager response to the words of Jesus as he pricked their consciences and called them to deeper trust in God.

One Sabbath morning in Capernaum, Jesus and the four joined the throng attending the new white stone synagogue that fronted the lake. It was crowded with merchants and fishermen and with travelers from other cities. Everyone who was able was expected to attend, and, besides, word had gone around that the popular preacher Jesus of Nazareth would speak that morning. The congregation sang praises, were led in the prescribed prayers, and heard the reading of the law as was the custom. Then the ruler of the synagogue asked Jesus to explain the scripture lesson.

Jesus said to the congregation: "You know that it was told our people of old: 'You shall not kill. And he who kills shall be punished.' I say to you that he who is angry with his brother, who insults his brother, is liable to the judgment of God. Our laws teach us to bring our offering to the Temple. But I say to you: 'If you are offering your gift at the altar and remember there that your brother has something against you, leave your gift before the altar and go first and make peace with your brother. Then come and offer your gift and it will be an offering acceptable to God, for God looks on the heart.' We have been taught of old to love our neighbors and hate our enemies. But I say to you: 'Love your enemies, for God loves the just and the unjust alike. We are in his Kingdom when we are like him.' "

The people were astonished. "Moses gave us laws to guide us, but Jesus says God cares how we feel toward people in our hearts. He asks more than obedience to Moses' law. Against what was written in our sacred books in olden times Jesus sets his own word: 'But *I* say unto you!' " They found no fault with this attitude of Jesus. They felt in him a deep self-assurance that had no hint of arrogance. They knew he was helping them understand better what God's will had really been from the beginning. And his words provoked thought. Was hate in the heart really against God's law? There was so much hate in men's hearts! They said to one another: "He speaks with authority. He says what he knows. The scribes always have to look into one of their many books to see what we must do. He speaks with wisdom. Where did he learn so much wisdom?"

The interest was tense. Suddenly the listeners were startled from their thinking by the cries of a demented man who was in the congregation. Stirred by Jesus' influence and words and by the excitement of the people, he cried out: "Let us alone. What have we to do with you, Jesus of Nazareth? Have you come to destroy us evil spirits? I know who you are, the Holy One of God." Jesus spoke to the madness in the man as something quite separate from him: "Hold your peace and come out of him." The man quieted down, the wildness left his eyes, his mind cleared, and he was like other people. Those in attendance were still more amazed: "A new teaching is exciting enough, but Jesus has authority even over unclean spirits."

All day there was as much visiting and discussion as the Sabbath law permitted, and as soon as the sun set and the Sabbath was over, the blind and lame and crippled and sick of mind were brought to Simon Peter's house where Jesus was staying. As night came on, the people kept coming, lighting their way with lamps and torches. It seemed as if all the city were gathering at the door. Jesus cured many, for their faith was great and it grew as he assured them, "It is your faith that has made you well." When the throngs finally left, Jesus was aware of a danger to his mission. Suppose the things the Spirit of God was working through him caused people to think no further than the deeds they could see? He would be popular with them, but that kind of popularity would be a hindrance to the work God had sent him to do. So the next morning Jesus rose early, long before dawn, and went into the hills to pray.

Presently he saw Simon Peter and the others coming to him. "They are all looking for you in the city," they reported. But Jesus did not respond as they expected. He led them in another direction, away from Capernaum. "I must preach the good news of the Kingdom of God in other cities also," he said, "for that is what I was sent to do."

He set out with them on a tour of the cities of Galilee, but his fame went far beyond his home province. From far and near the people came, farmers and laborers, traders and housewives, the unemployed and homeless, and a sprinkling of the rich and learned, of Pharisees and scribes. Among the scribes and Pharisees were those who appreciated Jesus, but most of them were critical and disturbed when they perceived the attachment of the people to him. The things he did and taught made them uneasy, and they watched him with exasperated interest.

The people gathered from Judea and from Syria and from beyond the Jordan River to hear Jesus, and to bring him the lame and blind and crippled and those who suffered from all sorts of diseases. "Your faith has made you whole," he would say when he healed them. There was a leper who called to him, "Master, if you will, you can make me clean." In pity for the man, disregarding all danger of defilement, Jesus touched the leper and cured him. "Go to the priests as the law provides," Jesus directed. The man obeyed, but he was too excited and stirred to pay attention as Jesus added, "And say nothing of this cure to anyone." The man spread the story abroad to all who would hear it, and the crowds about Jesus became still greater. Again Jesus went alone into the desert to pray.

After a time Jesus asked Levi, a tax collector, to join his disciples, and Levi left all and followed him. A tax collector! Perhaps he was good at heart, this Levi; perhaps he was just, this particular tax collector, but it was unpatriotic to make friends with those who worked for the Roman government. Jesus was taking to himself power that was not his, the Pharisees were saying among themselves. How about that cure when, undismayed by the crowd, some friends let down their paralyzed neighbor through the roof? "We all know that sickness comes from sin," the Pharisees said, "and perhaps that man was specially sinful, worrying about something he could not make right. But how dared Jesus say to him, 'Your sins are forgiven,' when the man was not first offering the penance the law requires! And as if Jesus had a special God-given right to do what only God may do or the priests in His name! Forgive sins indeed!" And then Jesus had cured the man. The paralytic had gone off, carrying his pallet rolled on his shoulder, walking as well as anyone. Bitter thoughts were in the minds of Jesus' critics. "Something must be done about it! Such success has made the crowds think this rabbi has the right to forgive sins. It docs not occur to them that his power over sickness may hail from Satan! None seem to criticize him. The rabble think everything he does is right!"

These critics had no reason for concern over Jesus' reception in his home town, however, when at last he went to Nazareth to preach. The Sabbath started well enough. The citizens of Nazareth came to the synagogue as was their custom, hastening their steps in anticipation of hearing their famous townsman. The attendant brought forth the roll of the Prophet Isaiah, and Jesus turned to the verses that said: "The Spirit of the Lord is upon me, because he anointed me to preach good tidings to the poor. He hath sent me to proclaim release to the captives and recovering of sight to the blind, to set at liberty them that are bruised, and to proclaim the acceptable year of the Lord." Then he went on: "The time of which the prophet spoke, the acceptable year of the Lord, has come. The day of the Lord is here. Salvation has come for the sick of body and mind, and for those bound by sin. The Kingdom of God is in your midst."

The people of Nazareth resented these statements. Anger rose within them. "Didn't he grow up among us?" they protested to each other under their breath: "How does this son of Joseph the carpenter dare take such importance to himself? What has he to do with the Kingdom? What he talks about is not what we are looking for." In their resentment they rebuked him. They said: "We hear of many mighty works you do in Capernaum. Why do you do none in your home town?" Jesus was deeply wounded in his spirit, but he had a quick answer from the scriptures. "In the great famine in Elijah's day, you remember, the prophet was not sent to an Israelite home but to a Sidonian widow. And the leper whom the prophet Elisha cured was not an Israelite but a Syrian." His fellow townsmen knew what Jesus meant to say. Faith is what counts before God, not what nation you belong to or where you live. But they were so incensed that they rose up against him, thinking to cast him down the precipice on the side of the hill on which their city stood. But they did not dare to touch him and he left Nazareth and did not return. Jesus remembered how Jeremiah was cast out of Anathoth by the anger of his kinsmen and neighbors. "A prophet has no honor in his own country," he commented sadly to his friends.

What happened in Nazareth brought the conviction to him that he must do more than teach in synagogues and preach to the crowds on the hills and the seashore. To fulfill his mission he would need a small, carefully trained group of disciples. Like Isaiah of old, he turned to a remnant; to the friends whom he had called in the early days in Capernaum he added others, to make twelve in all, chosen from among those who had responded to his teaching. This band of twelve left everything to associate themselves with him.

Often Jesus spoke to the Twelve in parables, explaining things about the Kingdom of God which the crowds would not understand. Nor did the disciples understand all that they remembered and kept thinking about. "The Kingdom," Jesus explained, "does not come with outward power and might. It is like a mustard seed, beginning from the smallest of seeds, and growing into a tree under which the birds of the air find shelter. It is like yeast in dough, working quietly until the whole mass is changed. It is like a sower who sowed seed, some of which fell on hard ground and some among thorns, but some of which brought forth much fruit. Not everyone can enter the Kingdom." One day at the edge of the crowd there was a disturbance. "It is your family come for you," was the message to Jesus. "Those who seek to know God's will and to do it are my family," he said.

"How much he counts on his followers, particularly on us!" his disciples thought. One thing they knew was necessary if they would be his disciples: they needed to live in God's presence.

The disciples remarked how often Jesus sought communion with God. They were accustomed to seeing the leaders of their people addressing God in prayer at street corners and other public places because the prayer time prescribed by law had come. They observed that in contrast prayer was a constant need of Jesus' life. So they asked him, "Master, teach us to pray."

"When you pray, say: 'Our Father, hallowed be thy name. Thy Kingdom come. Thy will be done,' " he answered. "Let those prayers come first, then ask the Father: 'Give us this day our daily bread. Forgive us our debts as we forgive our debtors. And lead us not into temptation but deliver us from evil.' "

"Forgive"—the word echoed in their minds. It was often in Jesus' speech. It must be very important to him that they learn to forgive. Peter asked, "Master, if my brother sin against me, is it enough if I forgive him seven times?" "Not seven times, but seventy times seven!" was the answer. "You can never set a limit to the forgiving you will do if you are my disciples."

During all this period of time while Jesus' influence was growing, John the Baptist was in prison. Herod Antipas, who ruled over much of Palestine, had put him there, fearing his influence and resenting his criticism. John had had such great expectations of a glorious new day. To stay in prison and, though guiltless, to lose hope of liberation—even John's courageous spirit faltered. "The Kingdom is near," he had proclaimed, "coming in power and making right triumphant." Then John began to think, "If Jesus was sent of God, must he not by now have brought in God's rule, destroying all evil?" So John sent some of his disciples to Jesus to tell of his worry and his doubt: "Are you the one who is sent of God, or must we wait for another?" Jesus answered: "Tell John the things you see and hear, how the blind receive sight and the lame walk, the lepers are cleansed, the deaf hear, and the dead are raised up. Tell him how the poor have good tidings preached to them. He must not be distressed if things are going differently from what he expected." That was Jesus' way of saying to him, "Yes, the Kingdom is here, but it is of a different nature from that which you had in mind." To his disciples Jesus said: "John is the greatest of all the prophets. But he could only look forward to that which you are in fact experiencing. You are seeing the Kingdom come."

They did not understand exactly what Jesus meant, but what he did and what he said and what he was had actually brought God's rule to them. They saw Jesus live in complete trust that God answers every need. They knew it was true when he said, "It is my meat to do the will of him that sent me." It was also apparent that he had a right to say, "God is working through me," for the Spirit and power of God were bestowed upon him in unusual measure. The Twelve had seen great things happen. They would see greater; of that they were sure.

III. *"Blessed is he who takes no offence at me!"* *

IF THE Kingdom Jesus proclaimed were to come to people, they had to meet its coming in faith and repentance. They had also to make a decision in relation to him. That is what the words mean: "It is for judgment that I came into the world." As time went on, the hostility to Jesus grew, as well as the devotion to him.

H E IS old enough to answer your questions for himself; ask him!" That is what the parents of the young man who had been born blind said to the Pharisees who were inquiring concerning him. Jesus had cured him on a recent Sabbath Day. "Was he really born blind?" the Pharisees asked. "Just what did Jesus do? How did he go about curing your son?"

The father and mother knew well enough what had happened, but they feared that they might be expelled from the synagogue if they acknowledged their gratitude to Jesus for a cure their

---

* Revised Standard Version.

leaders considered a defiance of the Sabbath laws. So they would
tell no more than to say: "He is really our son, about whom the
people are talking, and he was born blind. How he came to see
we do not know."

When the Pharisees talked with the young man, they said:
"You say this Jesus cured you, but he is not from God, for he
does not keep the Sabbath. We know that God has spoken to
Moses, but as for this man Jesus, we do not know where he comes
from! Give God praise! We know that this man is a sinner!"

The youth, glorying in his new sight and in his acquaint-
ance with Jesus, exclaimed: "He has opened my eyes, and yet you
do not know where he comes from? If he were not from God, he
could do nothing! Because he does God's will, God listens to
him!" They retorted, "You were born in sin and yet you think
you can teach us!" and expelled him from the synagogue. Seeing
that Jesus had opened to him a new way to live, the young man
from that time followed him.

The Pharisees had not been so drastic as this before. They had
gradually become more anxious to curb the influence of Jesus
because, they said, "He makes the law of no effect!" They could
not see that Jesus loved God's law even more than they did and
was rejecting only the man-made rules which were contradictions
to God's law. Jesus knew that some of their traditions were
mere forms. "You cancel out the law of God with these traditions," he said, but they could not understand such judgment.
In their minds, whatever their lawbooks required was God's
law.

"Does he not know," they would say to one another in exaspera-
tion, "that all over the world, wherever Jews live, the keeping of
the Sabbath is our people's pride?" Since the days of captivity the
Sabbath laws had been the badge of the Jews' religion. Many
rules had come to be accepted as part of the law, "Thou shalt remember the Sabbath Day to keep it holy." Rather than disobey any of them the Jews were glad to suffer indignity and ridi-
cule from gentiles who knew nothing of a sacred day.

There had been other times when Jesus or his disciples had
disregarded rules that seemed important to the scribes and Pharisees, rules regarding fasts and ritual washings, but what appeared

to them disrespect for the Sabbath roused their fury in special measure. It seemed a blow at the heart of their religion.

One Sabbath morning, Jesus' disciples had come through a cornfield with him. Being hungry, they plucked some grain, rubbed it in their hands, and ate it. They felt no guilt, for the law of Moses provided for hungry people on journey. The law said, "When you come into your neighbor's standing corn, then you may pluck the ears with your hand." It was because they were plucking the grain on a Sabbath that the leaders were angry. The law said that one might not reap or thresh grain on a Sabbath, and plucking and rubbing, the leaders said, was the same as threshing and reaping. "How can you let them do it?" they protested to Jesus. "The men are hungry; they need food!" he answered. "Don't you remember how David and his companions, when they came hungry to the house of God, ate some of the shewbread that it was lawful for only priests to eat? And the Sabbath—it was made for man, not man for the Sabbath!"

Some Pharisees had sat in the synagogue with expectant eyes that morning, for there was a man in the congregation who had a withered hand. "If Jesus breaks the Sabbath and heals this man, we shall have cause to accuse him!" Aware of their thought, Jesus was grieved that they could be so hardhearted, and looked at them angrily. He said to them: "What man is there among you who would not pull his sheep out of the pit if it fell in on a Sabbath Day? Of how much more value is a man than a sheep!" To the man he said, "Hold forth your hand," and when, in faith, the man held out his hand, it was restored to health. "It is not as if the man had been at point of death," the Pharisees said among themselves, "not as if he could not have been cured just as well a day later, when the Sabbath was over."

They thought the same about a cure on another Sabbath. When Jesus noticed in the congregation a woman who had been eighteen years a cripple, he called her to him. Putting his hands upon her shoulders, he said, "Woman, you are freed from your infirmity," whereupon the woman straightened herself. She was so filled with gladness that she immediately began to sing a song of thanksgiving. But the Pharisees said: "There are six days for work. Could he not have waited another day?" They went out to

plan how they could stop him. Meanwhile the people rejoiced
with the woman and were happy to have found a rabbi who did
not think the Sabbath must be a day of anxiety over the keeping
of rules.

There were among the Pharisees and scribes those who understood that Jesus was not a lawbreaker but that he was thinking of
a better way of keeping God's law. One of them who was trying
to get at the heart of the matter asked, "Which is the greatest of
all commandments?" Jesus said, "The greatest of all is, You shall
love the Lord your God with all your heart and mind and soul
and strength; and the other is equal to it, You shall love your
neighbor as yourself." The scribe said, "You are right—to love
God truly and to love one's neighbor is better than burnt offerings and sacrifices." Jesus said to him, "You are not far from the
Kingdom of God."

The company Jesus kept also exasperated the critical ones
among the leaders. He seemed to feel no responsibility for
upholding the standards one might expect of a rabbi, a teacher!
It was a scandal the way he enjoyed the company of publicans
and of other lawbreakers who were never to be seen in the
synagogues! It was a scandal the way he dined with them, visited
with them in their places of business, let them flock to him
when he preached! A glutton and a winebibber he was! They
must ask his disciples how he justified such actions! Jesus, knowing their questions, said to them: "Where do you think a physician ought to be? Not among the healthy, surely, while there are
those who are sick! I am sent to those who have made a failure of
life. Why spend my time, then, with righteous people like you?
There is more joy in heaven over one sinner who repents than
over ninety-nine who know no need of repentance!" They were
not quite sure what he meant by this. Was he suggesting that
they needed repentance too but were too blind to see it? Probably
he was; he would dare to do it. But surely this was turning things
upside down—to accuse good men of sin and at the same time to
be offering forgiveness to men who were known by everyone to
be sinners!

Over and over he forgave sins. Once a woman of ill repute
invaded the home where Jesus was having dinner with a friendly

Pharisee. As Jesus reclined on a couch, she came to weep over his feet and to dry them with her hair. "I have been taking him for a prophet, but I have been mistaken," thought his host. "A prophet would know that woman is a sinner. He would not let her touch him." Divining his thought, Jesus said to his host, "It is because much is forgiven her that she loves so much." To the woman he said: "Your sins are forgiven, your faith has saved you. Go in peace." "There he is again, forgiving sins. Who does he think he is?" commented the dinner guests to each other.

Who was he really? A prophet surely, but perhaps more than a prophet? The disciples too were thinking much about the question. "Is he Elijah come back? He says that God's Kingdom is here when God's will is done. He says too that it is coming, and that he is bringing it. And it is true that there has been no one like him in our history." Over and over again the disciples had heard men possessed of demons address him as the Holy One. Could they be right? Could he be the Coming One, the one their people had been expecting through the ages?

They remembered a woman among the Samaritans who thought so. On a recent journey the disciples had left Jesus resting at the well before the city of Samaria, and on their return found him in earnest conversation with a Samaritan woman. She presently hurried off to the city, leaving her water jar at the well, so eager to bring her friends and relatives that she forgot what she had come for originally. She said: "They must come too and see if this is not the Messiah we are expecting. He told me all the things I ever did."

There were some who were attracted to Jesus because they were interested in the Kingdom he proclaimed, but they soon ceased to follow him when they saw how difficult it was. "I want to be your disciple," said one man, "but I cannot follow you while my father lives; he would not understand and he needs me." "You cannot be part of the Kingdom unless you are willing to give up everything for it," Jesus said, "even your family."

"The way to destruction is broad," he said, "and many walk upon it." He told the story of one who hoarded riches selfishly and then expected to take his ease, eating and drinking and being merry. To him God said, "You fool, you shall die tonight, and whose will be all that you have garnered?" Then Jesus added, "You have to be like the man who gave up everything he had that he might buy a pearl he wanted."

An eager young man whom Jesus loved asked him: "What must I do that I may enter the Kingdom? I have obeyed the Commandments from my youth up." Discerning the young man's trust in his riches, for he was well-to-do, Jesus said to him: "One more thing is necessary. Sell all you have and give it to the poor, and then come and follow me." The young man turned away sorrowfully, and Jesus mourned over him, saying, "It is hard for a rich man to enter the Kingdom of Heaven."

"How, then, can one be saved?" the disciples exclaimed, and Jesus answered: "With man it is not possible, but all things are possible with God. He will call people into his Kingdom from the east and from the west, from the north and from the south, and some who are last shall be first, and those that are first shall be last. Whoever does the will of the Father in heaven will enter the Kingdom."

The scribes did not like to hear any questioning of the superiority of their nation over all other nations. Were not all the children of Abraham God's people? At any rate, were not all Abraham's righteous children the people of God? How could any others be first? In fact, how could any Jew raise such a question? Did not the scriptures say: "What great nation is there that has God so near to them as the Lord our God is to us when we call upon him? And what great nation is there that has statutes and judgments so righteous as our law?" The scribes were outraged as the people in Nazareth had been.

One of the Pharisees named Nicodemus sometimes listened to Jesus from the edge of the crowd. He knew Isaiah had taught that only a remnant would be saved, not all the children of Israel. He knew that another of the prophets had said in the name of God, "My name shall be great from the east to the west; everywhere shall a pure offering be brought to me, for my name shall be great among the heathen." So Nicodemus came to Jesus by night and said to him: "Master, we know you are a teacher sent by God, for no one could do the things you do unless God were with him. The things you say about the Kingdom—they strike me as true." Jesus said, "Only if one is born again, only if one is completely changed so that God's Spirit lives in him, will he be in the Kingdom." Nicodemus went away more thoughtful still, but he did not dare show openly his approval of Jesus.

The multitudes crowded about Jesus, but they did not understand what he had come to do. They did not repent, they did not change their ways, but they wanted him to heal their sick, and they loved him because of his great compassion. If they could but touch him, they were glad.

Reports came to Herod the king that Jesus now had a great following, and that one day when he had fed five thousand, compassionate over their hunger, the people had wanted to make him king. Some friendly Pharisees came to him and warned him: "Better get away from here. Herod is looking for you to kill you." Herod had killed John in prison and he feared any popular movement that might make the Roman government uneasy. A clash with the authorities at this time would have robbed Jesus of time he wanted to prepare the disciples for the difficult days he knew were ahead. And there was danger in his rising popularity. The crowds wanted to proclaim him the kind of messiah he was not and was never meant to be. Therefore Jesus said to his disciples, "Let us go away and rest awhile." So they went north, away from Herod's territory and away from the crowds.

In the region of Tyre and Sidon, out of Jewish territory, they walked together and talked together quietly. But not for long could they remain in seclusion, for even here Jesus was recognized. Some of the population who had seen him and heard him in Galilee and in Judea spread word of his presence, and soon the sick and the demented were being brought to him for healing. The needs of the people roused his compassion, for they had not the knowledge of God that his own people had inherited. But Jesus did not stay among them. He said, "I was sent to the lost sheep of the people of Israel," and he made his way back along the outskirts of Herod's territory.

Jesus wanted yet more time with his disciples, for he saw the days approaching when he and his disciples with him would have to stand alone. Good and evil men alike would try to stop them from doing the task God had given them. He led the Twelve through the open country toward the northernmost city of Israel, Caesarea Philippi. The population there was mostly gentile. Under Roman authority, and with many representatives of Rome among them, the people lived largely after the customs and religion of the Greeks. The small Jewish population was not given to strict observance of the Jewish laws.

"Shall we preach here?" The disciples who asked the question did not have to point out the need to their Master. There was also the possibility that here, where there would be little opposition, they might make swift headway. People starved for truth would respond quickly to Jesus' message. But to Jesus the time had not yet come to carry the Gospel to foreign peoples; his mission from God was to Israel. He had brought his disciples north out of the busy cities that he might prepare them to understand his mission better, and that he might help them to see the course it would be taking soon.

It was plain to Jesus that soon there would be trouble with the people because of the difference between their idea of salvation and the true salvation God had sent him to bring. He saw that they would not give up their hope for a messiah who would come as a mighty king to conquer all men for God. They would not accept God's true Messiah, whose victories were to be in the hearts of men.

Jesus saw suffering ahead, but the disciples still had their minds on a glorious future. Would their loyalty be tested too grievously? Some of the larger band of followers had left him, losing hope that he was bringing Israel salvation. The Twelve were devoted to him. Were they going to be loyal enough to be the remnant around which a new people of God might gather?

The lower slopes of the Hermon range were beautiful. Jesus and the Twelve walked along the streams, between small thickets of sycamores and mulberry trees and oleanders, or they skirted vineyards and fields of millet and wheat which clustered about quiet villages. Nature brought refreshment, but in Jesus' mind his future and that of his disciples loomed clear. He repeated many things he had previously taught them which would prepare them for that future.

One day, returning from an errand, they came upon him praying. They waited, and when he turned to them, he asked a startling question: "Who do people say that I am?" They were surprised, for always he had tried to turn away the enthusiasm of the populace from himself. He was in some way exceptional, they knew, and they had been pondering what it was that made him so. He was different. The Spirit of God filled his very being. They had been coming to a conclusion that was stirring them deeply. But he was asking, "Who do people say I am?"

"They say you are one of the prophets." Different ones of the band recalled the discussions they had heard among the people: that time, for instance, when Jesus had called Jairus' daughter back to life; when he had healed the sick; and sometimes when in a boat or on a hillside he sat teaching. "Some say you are John the Baptist come back, or one of the prophets of old, Elijah or Jeremiah, returned."

When they ceased speaking, Jesus asked searchingly, "Who do you say that I am?" Simon Peter spoke, and what he said expressed the faith that had been growing in the hearts and minds of all the disciples: "You are the Messiah, the Saviour whom God has sent. We know you are empowered of God to establish his Kingdom."

Jesus was gladdened by this declaration. "Blessed are you, Simon," he said. "You did not learn that of yourself. God has shown it to you." Then he warned them all, "Do not any of you tell it to the people, for it is not yet the time."

After this Jesus told the Twelve more plainly the things he had been preparing them to understand. The nation would not accept him as the Messiah, the Saviour sent of God. "It is a Suffering Servant whom God has sent to be the Messiah," he told them. "Do you remember how the prophet taught that a suffering servant would come, through whom Israel would be saved? Israel forgot his words among the many prophecies that looked to a future when God would rule." It sounded like a strange doctrine to the disciples, but if their Master said so, it must be true. "The time is near," he continued, "when the chief priests in Jerusalem and the scribes and the elders will reject me and kill me. On the third day," he added, "I will rise again." Their friend be taken from them? The Messiah be killed? None thought he had heard aright.

Peter was outraged, and he took Jesus aside and said: "How can you say such things? The Messiah die? God forbid that such a thing should happen to you!" Jesus answered sternly and firmly: "You are a stumbling block to me. What you say is not on the side of God but of men!" And he added: "It is not only I who will suffer. He who would follow me must be prepared to suffer also!"

Jesus now beckoned to the people who had been waiting for him, and when they came near, he taught them with the disciples, saying: "If anyone would follow me, he must deny himself. He who would save his life must lose it. What good is it to a man if he gain the whole world and lose his own soul?"

Peter was deeply troubled as he thought of Jesus' words. For some days the things Jesus had said concerning a sorrowful future were constantly in his mind. Could it possibly be that he was right? Peter talked with James and John: "Could such horror be? Was Jesus truly the Messiah whom God had sent if such things could really happen to him?"

Then Jesus took Peter and James and John up into the hills with him when he went to pray, as he so often did. As he prayed, the three friends saw a heavenly radiance about Jesus, and they beheld Moses and Elijah talking with him about his death that must come in Jerusalem. And from the radiant cloud they heard God's voice say: "This is my Son, my chosen one. Listen to him."

Peter's doubts were gone. It was so pleasant on the mountain that he wanted to stay there. The evil time seemed far off. Jesus told the three not to tell anyone what they had learned and seen on the mountain until he should have risen from the dead. They were puzzled. What could he mean?

When they came down from the mountain the next morning, crowds of people were waiting that Jesus might speak to them and heal their sick. There was a father among them whose son suffered from epilepsy, which the disciples had not been able to heal. He approached Jesus imploring, "If you can do anything, have compassion on us and help us!" Jesus answered: " 'If you can'! All things are possible to him who believes!" The father cried out: "I believe. Help my unbelief!" Jesus healed the lad, who went home with his father rejoicing. The disciples always remembered how the father's faltering eagerness had been recognized as faith by Jesus. They remembered also his words, in which he told them that they would have power to remove mountains of difficulty if they had faith even as a grain of mustard seed.

IV. *"Greater love hath no man than this, that a man lay down his life for his friends"*

To THE minds of Jews the Messiah was certain to be a conqueror against whom no enemies could stand. One prophet in Old Testament times saw clearly that to serve God faithfully and to speak his truth unswervingly among men always meant suffering for the one who did it, and that God used this suffering to win men to him. But no one ever took this to mean that the Messiah would have to suffer. Jesus, however, understood what was written, and knew that if he was to triumph as God's Servant he would have to be despised and rejected of men. The way to victory was the way of the cross.

"GIVE us a sign from heaven," the Pharisees demanded, hoping to prove Jesus a deceiver. "They say you are the Messiah sent of God. Do a miracle for us, and prove it!" Jesus was deeply grieved that they were so far from understanding his purpose. "There will be no sign except the sign of Jonah," he said, "the sign of repentance. Jonah brought God's message to Nineveh, preaching repentance, and the people of Nineveh repented." To his disciples Jesus said, "Beware of the influence of the Pharisees and Sadducees!" For the hardness of heart and the self-complacency of the Pharisees and the worldliness of the Sadducees kept them from seeing the truth.

The disciples went about teaching and healing in Jesus' name, but even they still expected a kingdom of signs and wonders that would bring Israel glory through a sudden divine act of power. Their great Teacher may often have been discouraged by their inability to grasp what he meant by the Kingdom of God. But he never wearied of explaining that God's Kingdom was already in their midst and yet at the same time coming in fuller glory.

Even James and John did not understand. They too still expected a kingdom of signs and wonders. One day they begged Jesus, "Master, promise that you will do for us whatever we ask of you!" Jesus asked, "What is it that you want me to do for you?" And they said, "Grant us the wish that we may be your two assistants, one on your right hand and one on your left, when you come to bring the Kingdom in glory." "You do not know what you are asking!" Jesus exclaimed. Observing that the other ten disciples were angry with James and John for their ambition to outrank them all, he called the Twelve to him and said: "You know that in worldly empires the great ones are those who lord it over the others, but let it not be so among you. Let whoever wants to be the first among you be the servant of all. I, your master, came not to be served but to serve."

At last, Jesus decided to leave Galilee, and he set forth resolutely to go to Jerusalem. He knew that a clash with the religious leaders would be inevitable. On the journey southward he explained many things he had told the disciples at Caesarea Philippi about the way in which he must fulfill his mission. "I am the Good Shepherd. A good shepherd gives his life for his sheep. A hireling leaves his sheep when the wolf comes, because he does not care for the sheep. I lay down my life for the sheep." The disciples listened attentively, but did not really see how heavily burdened was the mind of their Master. "I am distressed until it is all over," he said, "but I came to do the will of God who sent me."

News of Jesus' coming had spread over the countryside round

about Jericho. Bartimaeus, a blind beggar, was sitting by the road
to Jerusalem, listening. For many months his only hope had been
that sometime he would meet Jesus. Finally he heard an excited
hubbub, the kind of tumult that tells the approach of a multitude
of people. He called: "Is it Jesus of Nazareth? Is it Jesus?" "It is
he!" some bystanders informed him. Now he must gain attention!
Bartimaeus called through the crowd, "Jesus, son of David, have
mercy upon me!"

Son of David? That was the designation for the Saviour among
those who expected a warrior king, an earthly king who would
free Israel from foreign rule. A few persons disengaged themselves from the multitude to beg the blind man: "Be still! It is
dangerous to call that name!" Those who had some hope that
Jesus would disclose himself as that kind of messiah were most
eager to hush him. "Suppose some Roman heard you?" But Bartimaeus called all the louder, "Son of David, have pity on me!"

Jesus' voice was heard through the crowd. Some bystanders
encouraged Bartimaeus: "Cheer up! The Master is calling you!"
The blind man flung off his shabby cloak, lest it impede his steps,
and hurried in the direction of the voice he heard. Several of the
crowd steadied his steps as he approached Jesus and fell on his
knees before him. "What do you wish me to do for you?" How
could the Master ask? "O Master, that I might receive my sight!"
"Go your way," Jesus directed him, "your faith has healed you!"
Immediately Bartimaeus' eyes were opened, the long-hoped-for
gift of sight was his, and in gladness of heart he joined those
following Jesus. The tumult increased as the crowd perceived
what had happened. "This is the son of David! He has come!"
they shouted.

It was certain that a clash must come. This rising popular
enthusiasm would be dangerous. The leaders in Jerusalem would
think that Jesus was intending to make himself king over them.
Jesus yearned over the people: "If they but knew their salvation!"
All their thoughts were upon a kind of savior who could not save
anyone. Jesus decided the time had come when he must make
clear that he was indeed the Saviour sent of God. Till then he
had not said so in public. A number of times when those whom he
had cured had acclaimed him as messiah, he had commanded

them to be quiet, for it was important to him that people discover for themselves that he was sent of God.

Now the time had come when he must take a public stand to make clear what his mission was. Many people would not understand so unexpected a savior, many who were following would turn away disappointed, but there was hope that some might believe that he was truly the One whom God had sent to save his people.

Jesus sent two disciples to borrow a donkey from a friend, calling to mind one of the prophecies of long ago—the scribes would know it very well, even though they had not been thinking about it. The Anointed One would come into Jerusalem, according to this prophecy, not as a military conqueror on a war horse or in a chariot, but quietly and humbly, a man of peace riding on a donkey. "Rejoice greatly, O daughter of Zion," it read; "shout, O daughter of Jerusalem: here comes your king riding humbly on an ass!"

Pilgrims crowded the roads into Jerusalem, coming to the city for the celebration of the Passover, some of them from cities and towns in Galilee and the regions beyond Jordan through which Jesus had just come. These people knew him well. When they saw him come riding from Bethany toward Jerusalem, they began to shout their word for "God save the King!" "Hosanna! Hosanna!" they cried. "Blessed is he who comes in the name of the Lord!" They spread their garments on the road as for a royal procession, and waved branches, shouting: "Blessed is the kingdom of our father David! Hosanna in the highest!" They were giving Jesus a royal reception, believing he would bring in the Messianic Kingdom.

As he rode on, Jesus came in sight of the Temple on the heights of Jerusalem, the city where the religion of his people centered, a city unready and unwilling to accept the kind of kingdom he was bringing. The sight saddened him so that it drew tears from his eyes. He foresaw the future, when the ambition of the people would have brought destruction to the city, and he mourned: "If only you knew what would bring you peace! The days will come when not one stone will be left upon another, because you did not recognize what is for your salvation."

The people of Jerusalem asked, "Who is this that is causing such a stir?" The Pharisees and scribes, greatly troubled over the demonstration, debating what they might do against Jesus, exclaimed: "What can we do! All the world is gone after him." Some Greeks who had come to the city asked that they might know him. Everyone was speaking of him.

On that first day in Jerusalem, Jesus visited the Temple and watched the Passover pilgrims who were gathered there. He saw the Temple court noisy with the bleating of sheep, the cooing of doves, the traffic of porters, and the shouting of merchants who had concessions from the priesthood for the sale of sacrificial animals. People were milling about the tables of the money-changers, where the Roman coins of daily business were exchanged for the ones used in Jerusalem. Here was a magnificent building, erected by a king who cared nothing for the will of God. Here was a priesthood chosen because they were descended from Aaron, and considered fit to serve in the Temple because they had no physical blemishes. Here were offerings the ritual correctness of which was guaranteed by their purchase in the Temple courts. Jesus saw multitudes whose hearts were hungry for God's presence and for God's guidance in their lives being led in a worship that gave no true thoughts of God. As he left the Temple to go with the disciples to spend the night in Bethany, he recalled the worship of Jeremiah's day, when the prophet had declared the Temple unworthy of preservation because the worship in it had become a hollow form. It was worse now, when the religious leaders were making themselves rich from the transactions in the Temple courts.

The next day when Jesus returned to the Temple, he saw worshipers buying their sacrificial animals at unfair prices and exchanging their coins at exorbitant rates. What must a loving and righteous God think of these practices? Jesus looked at it all, and the falseness roused him to anger. He upset the tables of the money-changers and the stalls of those who sold doves, and he commanded all those trading in animals to stop selling. More to the Temple leaders than to the merchants he said, "Is it not written in the prophets, 'My house shall be a house of prayer for all people'? and you have made it into a den of robbers." To the hucksters and traders Jesus said, "Depart from here!" and his authority was such that they dared not disobey him.

The leaders responsible for the Temple worship were not slow in interpreting Jesus' words and actions. He was saying: "The worship in this place is not worthy of God. He has sent me to show a worthy way to serve him." He was acting as though he were in charge of the Temple. They decided that he must be stopped. What would the Jews in a Roman world be without the Temple and its worship? What would the leaders be without it? Their anger mounted because they could do nothing. The pilgrims from many lands were listening to this would-be reformer Jesus, and listening gladly. "If we arrest him," the leaders said, "there will be a great tumult and that will spoil the festival. There might even be a revolution."

The high priests and their associates conferred together day after day, but they could think of no adequate cause for arresting Jesus, and of no way to do it quietly. Perhaps they could trap him! Perhaps they could get him to say something that would discredit him with the people and involve him with the Roman authorities! So they heckled him on issues that were being much debated, but his straightforward answers gave his enemies no cause to accuse him. Neither did he seem to be calling upon the people to revolt.

There were some followers who wondered, "Is he going to be a disappointment after all?" After he came into Jerusalem he had wept and had spoken of destruction to come. Then he attacked the rulers of the Temple. But he did not attack the Roman government. And had he not even advised paying tribute to Rome? "Rome is your government, isn't it?" That is what his answer had amounted to when he was questioned concerning the payment of tribute. When some of the disciples had admired the Temple, its wonderful stones and carvings, he had said that the time would come when no two stones in the building would remain upon each other. Surely he was not planning to bring glory to Israel!

Judas, of the disciple band, felt his high hopes tumbling. Jesus, the Master of whom he had expected so much, seemed really to be heading for disaster. Was this the suffering he had been talking about? Judas felt cheated. He went to the leaders and said to them: "You are seeking to take Jesus without commotion? I will lead you to him so that you can arrest him, and you can do it on the charge that he is calling himself the Messiah."

Jesus spent his days visiting friends, making the most of the time with his disciples, teaching the people who thronged about him when he came into the Temple courts. At night he camped outdoors with his disciples, as did many of the pilgrims who came for the feast.

Always the disciples were on Jesus' mind, for they were the remnant who must carry out the mission that he had called them to share with him. He would bind upon their hearts what was most important. Before leaving them, he would weld them into a fellowship. He would have them know how much he loved them. He would prepare them against despair.

So he sent two of the disciples ahead into the city to make plans for supper in the home of a friend. "He will show you a large room," Jesus said. "There prepare the meal for us."

When the Twelve were gathered with him for the supper, to their dismay Jesus quietly took upon himself a servant's duties: he laid aside his outer garment, brought a bowl of water and a towel, and began to wash the feet of his disciples, one after the other. At first they were too much astonished to say anything. Then Peter, in his impulsive way, protested, "Master, you shall not wash my feet," but he submitted to Jesus' quiet, firm insistence. As Jesus circled the room, doing his lowly service, the disciples remembered again how they had quarreled concerning each one's rank in the Kingdom to come, debating who would be the greatest. Humbly they were learning, in this tense hour of expectation, that the only privilege Jesus was conferring upon them was the privilege of service, after his example. "Do as I have done to you!" he said to them.

As they were having supper, Jesus said to them, "One of you will betray me!" They were thunderstruck and very sorrowful. Not trusting themselves, they all asked: "Is it I, Master? Is it I?" Judas joined them in asking. "Surely it is not I, Master?" Jesus said to him, "Is it not?" Then Judas left the room and went out into the night.

Jesus took a loaf of bread, broke it into twelve pieces, and said a blessing over it. Then handing a piece to each of the disciples, he said, "Take, eat; this is my body." They took it wonderingly, sensing dimly what he was telling them. Then he lifted the cup of wine and handed it to the disciples in turn, saying, "This is my. blood, the blood of the new covenant, which is shed for many." The disciples were startled at the idea of drinking anything that represented blood, although they knew the cup contained wine. The law of Moses forbade the drinking of the blood of slaughtered creatures, repeating several times over, "The life of the flesh is in the blood." There they found his meaning. "I am giving my life for you and for many," was what Jesus was saying, and he was saying it in a way they could never forget.

"My blood is the blood of the new covenant!" A new covenant? What did Jesus mean? All their lives they had been taught that the daily sacrifices in the Temple and the Passover lamb and the atonement offering were for remission of sins, that Israel might keep the covenant and be the people of the Lord God. Jesus seemed to be saying, "In my death there is a new covenant with God!"

Jesus shocked them all by saying, "Before morning comes, before the cock crows, you will all be offended and leave me." Judas had left. How was it possible for a disciple to become untrue to the Master? Would they be tried beyond endurance? Just how hard were things going to be? But Peter said, "Even if everyone else is offended, I will not take offense!" Jesus answered, "I tell you truly, you will disown me this very night, before the dawn." Peter said, "Even though I have to die with you, I will never disown you." And all the others said the same thing.

As was the custom in Jewish households during Passover time, at the end of the meal they sang a psalm of thanksgiving, the Hallel: "O praise the Lord, . . . all ye people. For his merciful kindness is great toward us: and the truth of the Lord endureth for ever. Praise ye the Lord." Then they went to the Garden of Gethsemane on the Mount of Olives, across the Brook Kidron, where they had been accustomed to camp for the night.

When they arrived in the Garden, the disciples, except for

Peter and James and John, wrapped their mantles about them and went to sleep. Jesus guided the three to a more secluded spot. Knowing that his time was short, he asked these, his closest friends: "Will you stay here and watch while I go yonder and pray? My soul is deeply troubled, even to death!"

He liked to have them near, and they could guard while he prayed. But—they could not keep awake. In deep anguish of spirit, Jesus prayed. He knew what suffering was in store for him. Besides, Judas was failing him. Even sturdy Peter would find the night's experience too hard to bear. Was it possible that all Jesus' plans might be in vain? He prayed that he might escape the suffering that seemed to be before him, that perhaps another way might be found to fulfill his mission. "All things are possible to you, Father. Yet not my will, but thine, be done." In his prayer strength came to him, and a sharpened conviction that he was fulfilling God's mission through the suffering before him. Then he went to find consolation also in the company of his friends, but he found them sleeping.

As he wakened them, Jesus asked reproachfully, "Could you not watch one hour with me?" It was too late for sleep now. "Rise, for he who is betraying me has come." Out of the darkness appeared a company of the Temple police, headed by Judas and carrying swords and torches. Jesus asked them, "Whom are you seeking?" They answered, "Jesus of Nazareth," and were surprised to see him whom all this company had come to arrest present himself quite simply, saying, "I am he." As they were wondering how to arrest one so unresisting, he asked, "Why do you come out against me as if I were a robber, when I sat in the Temple daily?" And, pointing to the frightened disciples, he added, "If you are looking for me, let these who are with me go free."

Then his captors bound Jesus' hands. The disciples fled into the darkness as he was led away, but Peter kept the company ahead in sight. He followed at a distance and presently joined the soldiers and citizens who were warming themselves in the courtyard of the high priest's palace, where Jesus had been taken to appear before the council. Agreement of two witnesses was required for a death sentence. Various witnesses were brought forth to testify against Jesus, but their testimony was confused, and no two agreed on any charge. During all this time Jesus stood in silence, making no defense against all the false charges. Finally the high priest asked him point-blank the question all present had in mind. If Jesus acknowledged that he had claimed to be the Messiah, the Romans would interpret such claim as insurrection and condemn him to death.

"Are you the expected one, the Messiah?" Then Jesus broke his silence and said, "I am." The high priest tore his garment as a sign of horror and indignation, and exclaimed: "What need have we of more witnesses? You have heard how he has blasphemed God. What do you say?" And they all said, "He deserves to die!"

Meantime, beside the courtyard fire, Peter had been recognized by one who had seen him in the Garden: "You were with him. You belong to the company of the Nazarene!" Peter denied knowing Jesus. Then someone said: "But you are a Galilean, like he is. Your speech gives you away!" In his fright Peter shouted, "I tell you, I do not know him!" and he swore that he did not know Jesus. Just then Jesus was led by on his way to the Roman tribunal, and he looked at Peter. Reminded of his proud boast, that he would never, never disown his Master, Peter went out, weeping bitterly.

Pilate, the Roman governor, to whom Jesus had been brought for final judgment, was an ambitious man who did not want to arouse the people's disfavor lest they report to the Roman emperor some acts of his that would not bear investigation. He was favorably impressed with Jesus and was aware that the high priest's party were condemning him out of envy. Pilate's mind was torn between his belief in Jesus' innocence and the desire to please his accusers. "It cannot be denied," Pilate reasoned, "that they can make a case before a Roman tribunal, for this prisoner has said he is the Messiah, and that is the expected King of the Jews! Yet I know that this man has no intention of overthrowing the government!" Pilate wanted no dissension and yet he could not set aside his conviction that Jesus was an innocent man. Then he thought of a way out. At the time of the Passover festival, it was the custom for the Roman government to pardon a prisoner selected by the Jews.

Expecting that surely they would choose Jesus, Pilate offered the choice of Jesus or Barabbas, whom they knew as a rebel against Rome. The crowd that the high priests and their party had collected, with the citizens whose disappointment had turned into hate, heard Pilate's proposal, and his question, "Shall it be Jesus or Barabbas?" They cried out: "Give us Barabbas! Give us Barabbas!" Pilate asked, "What shall I do with Jesus, who is called King of the Jews?" They called: "Crucify him, crucify him! We have no king but Caesar!"

With a guilty conscience, but in fear of offending the Jewish leaders, Pilate turned Jesus over to the military authorities to be crucified. The soldiers took off his garments and lashed him with cruel whips. Informed that he was being put to death for saying he was "King of the Jews," they put a scarlet cloak about his shoulders and placed on his head a circle of thorny briers in imitation of the Roman emperor's crown of laurel leaves. Then they bowed their knees before him in mockery, saying, "Hail, King of the Jews." The struck him in the face and spat upon him. Then they put his own garments back upon him and led him to Calvary to be crucified, bearing his cross upon his shoulders.

Some of the women, including Mary of Magdala and the mother of James and John, who belonged to the larger band of Jesus' disciples, followed at a distance. They saw Jesus break down under the burden of the cross. Simon, a Cyrenian, was called by the soldiers to carry it the rest of the way up the hill. There Jesus was nailed on the cross, with the inscription above him, "Jesus of Nazareth, the King of the Jews!" On either side of him were crucified two thieves.

Hour after hour went by while men scoffed, saying, "He saved others, but he cannot save himself." One of the thieves joined the crowd in mocking Jesus, but the other thief recognized in Jesus a dignity and a majesty that made him different. Himself bitter at heart, he had noticed how in all the terrible suffering Jesus had shown no trace of bitterness. Then he heard him pray, "Father, forgive them; for they know not what they do." Repentant, the thief begged of Jesus, "Remember me when you come into your Kingdom," and heard Jesus answer, "Today you shall be with me in paradise."

In the extremity of his anguish Jesus cried out, "My God, my God, why hast thou forsaken me?" Then he prayed, "Father, into thy hands I commend my spirit," and breathed his last.

The Roman centurion who was in command of the crucifixion stood in deep reflection before the cross. "Certainly this Jesus was a good man," he said. "It must be God sent him, as he said. He was the son of God!"

Nicodemus and another secret disciple of Jesus, Joseph of Arimathaea, were granted permission by the Roman authorities to give the body of Jesus burial. Mary Magdalene, and Mary Clopas, who also loved Jesus, were the only mourners in attendance. As the twilight fell, they sat grieving in Joseph's garden. In sorrow and confusion of spirit, they watched while the body of their friend was laid to rest in a new-made tomb.

The Master had died a criminal's death. Was this to be the end of the Kingdom he had brought?

V. *"I am come that they might have life . . . and . . . have it more abundantly"*

THE disciples, who had waited for God's Kingdom to come in glory, were mourning over their crucified Master, all their hopes defeated. Then something happened to make them feel that God was saying to them: "I am back of all that Jesus said and did. My power is in him who was obedient in all things. His death on the cross was not defeat, but victory."

Two of the disciples were walking the wide road from Jerusalem toward the sea. At times they were lost in thought; again they were engaged in earnest conversation. After a while they turned to cross a stream, then took a path toward the town of Emmaus. There was still an hour's journey before them through a narrow gorge, then in a broad green valley. They were not noticing the landscape at all, were not seeing the pomegranate trees on the slopes, nor the olive trees beside the way. It was the third day after the crucifixion and they were heavy in spirit. So much had happened. So many things were changed. So many impressions crowded their minds and tried to find expression in speech. The men rehearsed to each other the happenings each knew so well: how the women who had watched the crucifixion from afar had been present at the burial in Joseph's garden, and stayed mourning till the evening when the Sabbath came; how Judas had hanged himself in remorse and despair; how Peter, who had disowned the Master, was brokenhearted. But none could shame him really, for had they not all fled? The two confessed to each other how cowardly they themselves had felt. But what could they have done had they stayed? The last thing to happen was that Mary Magdalene and Salome and the other women were saying that Jesus was risen from the dead. But that must be idle talk.

A stranger joined them. "You seem troubled and disturbed," he said. "Everybody is troubled and disturbed," they rejoined. "You must be a stranger in Jerusalem if you do not know all the things that have happened there this week." "What things?" "Concerning Jesus of Nazareth. We had hoped he was the Redeemer sent of God. His words and deeds made us believe so. Our chief priests and rulers thought otherwise, and they condemned him to death and crucified him. There is excitement among us today, for some of the women of our company who went to the tomb say that an angel told them he was alive. Some of us went to the tomb but did not see him."

"Have you not been reading the prophet?" the stranger asked. "He tells how God's servant must suffer. 'Despised and rejected,' the prophet said he would be. He had to bear all these things before he could enter into glory."

While they were conversing the three came to a crossroads and the stranger seemed to be going farther. Their hearts had gone out to him and they did not like to part from him, so they begged him, "Come with us, for the darkness is near, and you shall find your night's shelter with us." He accepted their invitation and went on to Emmaus with them. It was when they sat at supper that they were suddenly filled with amazement and glad surprise, for when their companion picked up the bread, broke it, and blessed it, they knew who he was. In the moment that they recognized him, he vanished from their sight.

Excited and with new energy, they hastened back to Jerusalem to find the other disciples. Before ever they could tell what had thrilled them, the disciples called to them: "The Master has risen from the dead! He has appeared to Peter!" The two Emmaus pilgrims could well believe it. "We saw him too!" they reported, and described how they had known him by the breaking of bread.

Then exclamations of wonder and awe broke from all the company. Jesus was standing among them! At first, for very surprise, they could not believe their eyes. Then he began to speak with them to reassure them. "It is I, myself. Why are you troubled?" Then, as they realized his presence, great gladness filled their hearts.

As to the two disciples on the road to Emmaus, Jesus explained to all of them the things that before his death they had been too preoccupied to understand. The Saviour had to suffer for the sins of men. God's love for mankind had caused him to send a Redeemer and Saviour who bore sin and death with them and for them. "The Holy Spirit will come upon you," he told them, "and you shall preach repentance and the forgiveness of sins in my name to all nations."

At still other times Jesus made his presence known to his disciples, and to others who had faith in him. He appeared also to his own brother James, who formerly had not believed in Jesus' mission but now became a leader among those who did believe. The joy of all of them was unspeakable. Not even when Jesus appeared to them for the last time were they saddened, for they knew he would be with them always. He said to them in parting: "Stay in the city until you are clothed with power from on high, for the Holy Spirit will come upon you, and in the power of the Spirit you shall be my witnesses in Jerusalem and in all Judea and in Samaria and in the uttermost parts of the earth. And I am with you always, even to the end of the world."

The faith of the disciples was so strong that nothing which doubting and critical people might say could shake it. They studied the scriptures with great zeal and saw written there that Israel could not save itself by observance of the law; that the great Servant of the Lord, himself innocent, would suffer, be "a man of sorrows, and acquainted with grief," "crushed for our guilt";

that he would be raised to glory because he had been obedient to death. How was it, they wondered, that they had not understood what Jesus was saying to them before he died, when he tried to explain what would happen!

The disciples met together daily, reading the scriptures with new understanding, praying together, as Jesus had taught them, "Our Father, thy will be done, thy Kingdom come." It all meant so much more than in the former days.

There were one hundred and twenty companions, including the eleven disciples, Jesus' mother and his brothers, Mary Magdalene, Salome, and the other women disciples, and others from among those who had followed Jesus during his ministry. Often they had supper together in Jesus' memory in the way he had told them to do. Peter was their leader. He remembered how Jesus had said to him before his death, "I have prayed for you that your strength may not fail, and you in turn must strengthen your brothers." The day now seemed far past when he had been afraid to say that he was a follower of Jesus.

Peter, James and John, Philip, Thomas, and the rest, understood their mission. They knew that they must use the experience Jesus had given them when he sent them forth by twos to heal and preach in his name, but they did not feel that they had as yet received the power of God's Spirit which Jesus had promised them. The disciples knew that through them people must learn of the mercy and grace of God as Jesus had showed it, and of life in fellowship with Him as Jesus had lived it. Daily they prayed that the Spirit of God that was in their Master would come to them as he had promised, making them ready for their task. "Did he not tell us," they reminded each other, "that in the power of the Holy Spirit we would be witnesses for him?"

At last their prayers were answered. It was the feast of Pentecost, the gladdest of all the Hebrew festivals. Pilgrims from all over Palestine, joined by pilgrims from far places, came to Jerusalem to offer thanks for the harvest. In the Temple courts, Jews from countries distant and near knelt in worship as the Levites played on silver trumpets, and sang psalms to the sound of harps. There were present Jews, with long curled beards, from Persia and Media; Jews from Babylon in the long mantles of their country; those from Rome wearing the toga of their adopted city; those whose garments betokened wealth; and poor Jews, with lean and bony limbs, whose deeply bronzed skin told of life in the Arabian wilderness. The disciples worshiped with them, then gathered quietly in their accustomed place of meeting. There they prayed together that God might use them for his purpose. It was then that the Spirit of God came upon them in such fullness that it possessed them. They could not do otherwise than go among the people and speak what was in their hearts. The holiday crowds marveled at the ardor and passion with which they spoke, and at the knowledge of scripture they showed: "How do these simple Galileans know so much?" As more and more people gathered, Peter stood forth on the Temple porch and preached to the crowd, proclaiming the Gospel, the good tidings of Jesus.

"Jesus of Nazareth, whom you crucified," he said, "through whom God made his way known as he walked among us, he is the approved of God, for God has raised him from the dead, as we are all witnesses. Let all Israel know that he it is whom God sent. Repent of the hardness of heart that kept you from knowing him as the Saviour sent of God. Be baptized in his name."

Many of the listeners from Galilee and Judea and across Jordan had known Jesus; others, even those from far places, had heard about him. They had been puzzled and disturbed by the crucifixion of one who had done so much good. Now Peter's words, spoken in the power which God's Spirit gave him, persuaded them that in Jesus they would find their Redeemer and Saviour.

Large numbers said to themselves: "Our hearts told us rightly about Jesus. We want to learn from him and dedicate our lives to God's service, following after him." They asked to be baptized, and they joined themselves to the disciples to follow Jesus' way. The group came to be known among themselves as "the disciples," or "the followers of the way," or as "the believers." The other Jews spoke of them as "the sect of the Nazarenes." The original disciples were their leaders, and were now called "the apostles," or "the Twelve." To take Judas' place, Matthias had been selected from among those who had followed Jesus and had seen him after the resurrection.

These believers lived according to the laws of the Jews and worshiped in the Temple and the synagogue with their neighbors and friends after the customs they had known since childhood. But the meetings that were most important to them were those they attended as disciples of Jesus. There they broke bread together and explained to each other the things Jesus had done and said. Together they thanked God for the joy in life that was theirs since in Jesus' life and death and resurrection they had come to know God's mercy and forgiveness. In loyalty to Jesus and in the power of the Holy Spirit they lived in harmony, serving each other.

For a time there was no friction with the authorities. The populace, observing the growing company of disciples, was glad to see their joy and happiness.

One day when Peter and John went to the Temple, a lame man who spent his days begging at the entrance known as the Beautiful Gate, asked them for alms. "Silver and gold I have none," said Peter, "but what I have, I give you." Through faith, as Jesus had done, and in Jesus' name, he cured the man of his lameness, so that a crowd gathered to see one they had long known as a cripple walking and leaping and rejoicing, thanking God. Peter could not forego the opportunity of preaching when he saw people gathered. He proclaimed the name of Him after whose example and in whose power the lame man had been made well.

Then he went on to say: "And this Jesus, of whom we are telling you, is the one expected by our people from the days of Moses, and even before that. You remember how God promised Abraham that through his descendants all mankind should be blessed. It is Jesus who brought that promised blessing, when he came on earth to show God's love and forgiveness and to make known how we can serve Him in truth. Repent of the sin of rejecting Jesus and be converted to follow him."

Some of the followers of the high priests who were troubled to see Peter and John's influence among the people arrested them. They put them in prison overnight, and brought them before the council. Peter and John stood before the leaders without fear and began to speak of their joy in being chosen to proclaim the Gospel of Jesus: "You ask us in what power and in whose name we do these things. It is in the name of Jesus of Nazareth, whom you crucified and whom God raised from the dead, that this man who was lame stands before you well."

The council were in a quandary. They wanted no preaching about Jesus, but they feared to imprison the apostles because of the people's interest in them. Therefore the judgment was, "The prisoners may be freed, but they must promise to speak no more of this man Jesus."

Peter and John would make no such promise. "You must judge for yourselves," they declared, "if we should obey you rather than God. We cannot do otherwise than speak of the things we have seen and heard." Then the council let them go, not knowing what else to do with them.

At another time when Peter and John were put on trial, Gamaliel, a greatly trusted leader among the Pharisees and a renowned teacher of the law, advised those who would imprison the two apostles: "Let them alone. If their work is of men, it will come to nothing; but if it is God's work, you cannot overthrow it. You might be found fighting against God." So Peter and John were released and went back to the other disciples, praising God that they had had opportunity to suffer indignity for Jesus' sake.

No one among the believers suffered want, for they shared all possessions, the rich dividing with the poor. Among them were many who spoke Greek, for Greek was the language of trade and government in Palestine. Some of these were people who had lived in other parts of the Roman Empire and had returned to live in their homeland. Some came from Decapolis beyond Jordan, where Greek was the language of daily speech. The language of most of the Christians in Galilee and Judea, however, was Aramaic. In the Greek-speaking minority of the congregation were those who believed that their widows and orphans were less well provided for than were those who spoke Aramaic. The apostles called a meeting and said: "If we are to preach what we saw and learned when we were with Jesus, we cannot also serve tables. One or the other of these tasks will not be done well enough if we must do them both. Will you choose people of wisdom, in whom the Spirit of God dwells, that they may be our helpers?" The choice that was made showed the good will of the believers, for all the helpers chosen, Stephen, Philip, and five others, were people with Greek names. They were entrusted with the care of the Aramaic and the Greek-speaking widows and orphans alike.

One of the helpers, Stephen, began also to preach the Gospel of Jesus. That is how it happened that he was one of the first to learn what Jesus meant when he warned his followers that there would be suffering to bear in his name. Stephen went into the synagogues in Jerusalem where those who spoke Greek gathered. He gained many new disciples there, for he was very convincing in his own strong faith, but he also found opposition. Attending the Greek-speaking synagogues were some who were inclined not to take seriously all the rules taught by the scribes. These people did not believe that everything that happened in the Temple was necessary to the worship of God. But most of the members obeyed the regulations scrupulously. They had come back from other lands in order that in Palestine they might more readily obey the laws of their people in all exactness and so win favor with God. In foreign lands, where they had had a chance to observe heathenism, they had learned to value their own religion, and they cherished every part of it.

When Stephen told approvingly how Jesus had spoken to the scribes and Pharisees who criticized him for healing on the Sabbath, these worshipers became as angry with Stephen as once those scribes and Pharisees had been toward Jesus. And when Stephen repeated Jesus' saying that one day the Temple would be destroyed, so that not one stone would remain on the other, their anger knew no bounds. They brought Stephen before the council and accused him of blasphemy, reporting, "He said that Jesus of Nazareth will destroy the Temple and will change the customs Moses has taught us."

The high priest asked Stephen, "Is this so?" Then Stephen, filled with the Spirit of God, began to speak all that was in his heart. He told the story of the people of God—how, from the days of their forefather Abraham, God had led them and taught them through the things that happened in their history and by the word of Moses and the prophets. Moses made a Tabernacle after God's commandment and Solomon built a Temple, Stephen reminded them, but did not the prophets teach that God is greater than temples made with hands? "Heaven is my throne," the Lord said, "and the earth is my footstool, but I live in the heart of him who is of a contrite spirit." Would God perish when a building of wood and stone was destroyed?

"When you resisted Jesus of Nazareth," Stephen said, "you were like your forefathers who resisted God's prophets, only you have resisted Him whom the prophets foretold, the Righteous One sent of God."

At that the crowd which had gathered became so angry that shouts were heard threatening Stephen's life. Thinking of the danger only as a cross he would gladly bear in Jesus' name, and filled with the Spirit of God, Stephen looked toward heaven and said, his eyes shining, "I see the heavens opened to show the glory of God, with Jesus standing at his right hand."

Then a riot broke out. Without court trial, Stephen was hurried to the edge of the city, to the place where those convicted of blasphemy were stoned. There some of his accusers laid their outer garments for safekeeping at the feet of Saul of Tarsus, one of their sympathizers, while they stoned Stephen. As Stephen died, he was heard to pray: "Lord, do not hold this sin against them. Jesus, receive my spirit!"

Fear an dismay spread among the grief-stricken Jerusalem disciples. Their danger increased through a persecution organized by Saul. He was a freeborn Roman citizen of Jewish birth and zealous in the worship of the God of his fathers. He had come to Jerusalem from the great merchant city of Tarsus, in Cilicia, that he might study Jewish law under the famous teacher Gamaliel. "It is clear," Saul argued, "that God has pronounced his judgment upon this Jesus, for does not the law say, 'He that is hanged is accursed of God'?" So Saul secured letters from the authorities empowering him to commit "the Nazarenes" to prison.

The disciples scattered far and wide to escape persecution, but not to hide their allegiance to Jesus. The memory of Stephen's martyr death fired their enthusiasm to bear witness to their faith. Wherever they went, the contagion of their faith and courage brought others to the decision that they should live as Jesus' followers, in ready obedience to the will of the loving God whom Jesus had revealed.

Stephen's friend and co-worker Philip became a missionary in Samaria. Some of the believers went to Antioch and preached there. Others fled to Damascus in Syria. There Saul presently went to search them out that he might bring them to judgment.

VI. *"If any man be in Christ, he is a new creature"*

AGAIN, God's ways were surprising. As the Redeemer came in a manner no one had anticipated and fulfilled his mission in unexpected ways, so the apostle who did the most to spread his Gospel arose most unexpectedly from among those who had believed Jesus a blasphemer and a danger to the true worship of God. Like the prophets of old, this apostle explained the meaning of God's acts in the history of his people. He proclaimed that the long-hoped-for salvation had come.

As SAUL journeyed to Damascus, his mind was in turmoil. This new sect of the Nazarenes was a threat to true religion. The devotion of Stephen and the others to a crucified one was a madness that must be stamped out! It was not easy to take your own compatriots to prison! Saul had gained the energy to arrest his fellow Jews from his devotion to God and to his people. God was sending him to these misguided ones to prevent them from injuring the whole nation. Yet—he could not forget Stephen, his joy in dying in the name of Jesus, and the words he had spoken when he proclaimed his faith.

"In crucifying Jesus," Stephen had said, "our people did again what they have so often done in the past. They rebelled against God's will, as they did when they would not listen to the prophets of old."

The religion of his people was Saul's pride. He had grown up among the confused, lawless, unhappy populace of a heathen city where many gods were worshiped and he knew how to treasure his religious inheritance. Through it he had come to know the one righteous and holy God who ruled the world. But Saul's faith had not brought him happiness. All his life he had tried to earn God's favor, but somehow he had never found the peace he sought. Stephen's face as he met death had expressed a peace beyond understanding. And the disciples Saul had imprisoned since that day—they had gloried in the opportunity to suffer for the Gospel of the man they called their Master, who they said was risen from the dead. They seemed to have this strange peace too. It troubled him to think of them!

Saul's mind dwelt upon the Nazarene. This Jesus had taught God's love for all people. He was not to be condemned for that. The prophets long ago taught God's boundless mercy. There were many fine things in the Nazarene's teachings and much that must be admired about the man himself. But his attitude toward the law and the Temple! That was where the trouble began! Revising the law of Moses! Soon there would be no law of Moses if men began tampering with it as Jesus did. And then his claim to be the Messiah! A Messiah dying a criminal's death on the cross! And now his followers were trying to escape the shame of this death by making the ridiculous assertion that he had risen from the dead!

Saul knew what a danger people with such absurd and revolutionary ideas might be to the future of his nation. The Jews were a small people. Repeatedly they had been in danger of extinction. Rome was so very strong—it might absorb Israel. The influence of the culture of this world empire upon the population was evident even now. Many of the cities of the land were full of pagans. At so critical a time to have a sect arise that might adopt

their master's attitude toward the law and the Temple! To regard
lightly this danger to Israel's religion from within the people of
God would be treason to the God of the fathers. There was nothing for it but to root out the sect. Surely God would guide his
servant in the difficult duty before him!

Such were Saul's thoughts as he journeyed along with his companions and was nearing the city of Damascus. Suddenly he felt a
blinding radiance envelop him and he dropped to the ground.
He heard words and saw a vision of which his companions were
not aware, yet nothing in his life had ever been more real to him.

"Saul, Saul, why do you persecute me?"

"Who are you?" Saul asked.

The answer came: "I am Jesus, and you are persecuting me.
Get up and go into the city. There you will be told what you are
destined to do."

Saul's pride was shattered. Now he knew what the Nazarenes
in Jerusalem had been talking about. He too had seen the living
Jesus and had heard his voice. He too knew that Jesus was not
dead but alive. He had no doubt about that.

For three days Saul did not leave the house in Damascus, in the
street called Straight, where he lodged. Fasting and praying, he
sought to know God's will. Then Ananias came to him, addressing Saul, his persecutor, as a brother. "Brother Saul, the God of
our fathers willed that you should see the Righteous One and
hear his voice, for you are to tell of him not only to Israel but to
all men. Arise and be baptized, that your sins may be washed
away; and ask the Lord to guide you."

Saul was baptized and introduced to the disciples. In the days
that followed he asked them many questions about the things
Jesus had said and done. Then he went into the wilderness and
remained there for a time to meditate and to pray.

Obeying the law had been his life. Now he saw that obedience
to the law was not enough. God's love, as he found it in Jesus,
filled his spirit and created in him a love toward others that made
him do much more than the law ever required. Saul now saw in
Jesus what God originally wanted man to be, His son, fit for fellowship with him. And in Jesus he also saw what God is like, so
eager to win man to himself that no price is too high, not even the

death of his Son on the cross! It seemed to Saul that for the first
time he knew the depth of man's sin. How terrible is sin to cause
so great pain and sorrow! But how great God's mercy and how
needful, since none was good enough to obey God's law! A great
weight fell from Saul's shoulders as love for God came into his
heart. He could not express the gratitude he felt. Oh, the riches of
the wisdom and love God had shown him through Jesus! He
would give his life to making Jesus known so that others might
have him as their Saviour too. Saul was a new man, so that he
could say, "I no longer live for myself, but for Him whose love
controls me."

Saul returned to Damascus and began to preach there, but so
much hostility was aroused among the Jewish inhabitants, who
resented his change of heart, that his life was in danger. His
enemies watched for him at the city gates but his friends thought
of a way to get him out of the city undetected. They let him down
in a basket from a window in the city wall and he hastened away
to Jerusalem. When he arrived, he sought at once the companionship of those who shared his devotion to Jesus, but none of them
trusted him. Had he not arrested their brothers and sought to
stamp out the fellowship of the believers? Only Barnabas of
Cyprus knew that Saul was a new man, that he had risked his life
in Damascus preaching the Gospel of Jesus. Barnabas introduced
Saul to Peter, who invited him to stay in his home for a time and
took him to meet James, the brother of Jesus. Peter and James
had heard from disciples in Damascus of Jesus' appearance to
Saul, and they had concluded, "God must have great plans for
Saul's future." Now they could see for themselves in every word
and action of Saul's that he wanted nothing in life but to help
others know God through Jesus, as he himself had come to know
him.

Peter and James could not tell enough to Saul of all that Jesus
had said and done in his life among his people. Saul could not
testify enough to them of his joy in knowing Jesus' willingness to
die and thereby show God's mercy toward men. "God has revealed to me in Jesus the Gospel I must preach," he said. Saul
began to preach in Jerusalem, but the feeling there was too strong
against him. Humbly he prayed to God for guidance, and the

answer he received was, "Go, I will send you afar." Remembering
Jesus' words charging his followers to tell his Gospel "unto the
uttermost part of the earth," Saul accepted it as his mission to
carry the message as far as God would lead him. Some of the disciples accompanied him to Caesarea, where he took ship for
Tarsus, to preach in his home province of Cilicia. Soon the disciples in Jerusalem had word of his vigorous and effective preaching and they thanked God for the power of God's Spirit shown
in Saul.

Barnabas, now active in the great city of Antioch, also gloried
in his friend Saul's faith and work and invited him to help in the
ministry to the disciples there. They were a large group, both
Jews and gentiles, which had grown from those who fled from
Jerusalem to Antioch at the time Stephen was stoned. They were
the first to be called "Christians." The name was given to them
by the citizens of Antioch, who often heard them speaking the
name of "Christ," the Greek word for "Messiah." The nickname
was accepted by the disciples and became their pride and Saul's,
who said, "I know nothing but Christ and him crucified." Among
these Christians in Antioch Saul worked and preached for some
years.

As at Jerusalem, the disciples in Antioch desired to spread the
Gospel. Presently, at a prayer meeting, they were guided to send
forth Barnabas and Saul, who had come to be known as Paul.
(Saul was his Jewish name; Paul, his gentile one.) Barnabas and
Paul crossed first to the island of Cyprus, where Barnabas had
once lived. Encouraged by the interest their preaching aroused,
they decided upon a more daring expedition into Galatia, the
central province on the mainland of Asia Minor.

The rugged mountain passes of Galatia, edged by forests of
cypress and laurel, were not easy to travel. At last Paul and Barnabas arrived at Antioch of Pisidia, the largest city of the region,
and were received with gladness. Visitors were all the more welcome because difficult travel made it hard for Jews in such distant
regions to keep in touch with happenings in Jerusalem. Paul was
particularly happy over the eager response of the congregation
when he told them that the Messiah, so long expected by the
Jews, had come. He explained how through Jesus of Naza-

reth God's promise to Abraham had been fulfilled: "Through your descendants shall all the nations of the earth be blessed." "All Israel's history has been a preparation for his coming," Paul said. "No matter how hard we tried, we could not by our own efforts win salvation. We never deserved anything except judgment from the righteous, holy God. But now the Redeemer has come and salvation is open to all who will believe. Jesus was crucified by men in their ignorance, but God has raised him from the dead. Through Jesus, God gives to believers the power of his spirit and newness of life. In sending the Redeemer, God has done for us what we could not do for ourselves in all our efforts to keep the law."

There were a number of people in the congregation whom the Jews called "God-fearers." They were not Jews by birth, but they were attracted to the synagogue when they saw the contrast between the dissolute lives of their fellow pagans and the clean and honest lives of the Jews. They soon learned to worship the one righteous and holy God, who was very different from the gods they had known in the past. These Galatians were particularly interested when Paul concluded by saying: "Through faith in Jesus people anywhere may be people of God. When they live according to the will of God, they are God's people. For that matter, being truly Abraham's descendant means having faith, for he is the father of the faithful."

Paul's message was heard with joy, and the leaders of the synagogue asked Paul to speak again on the following Sabbath. Meantime, more and more of the non-Jewish worshipers came to see Paul and Barnabas in their lodgings and to talk with them. "Many of our people would worship the God of Israel," they said, "but full membership in a Jewish congregation means obedience to laws that it is practically impossible for us to obey, laws that do not seem to us important." There were rules, for instance, against eating certain kinds of food, rules against Jews' living in the same house with non-Jews—hundreds of rules which it was hard even for a Jew to remember and obey.

Paul said to them: "You can be God's people even though you were not born as Jews and even though you do not keep all the Jewish laws. Christ has shown us a new way. It does not mean that we obey God's law less than others. Rather the opposite! If we are true believers in Jesus and let his Spirit dwell in us, we shall be filled with a love of God and of our fellow men which makes us do far more than the law requires."

Barnabas was less of an orator than Paul, but he was a great pastor of souls, and when members of the synagogue noticed the popularity of the two among the non-Jews of the community, they became disturbed. Meantime, they had thought more about the story of the Messiah who, their visitors said, had died on a cross. Their law said that those who died so were accursed. And why was it that the visitors from Jerusalem who came last year and the year before had not told them of the appearance of the long-expected One? When reports reached the leaders of the synagogue that many of the God-fearers were being baptized by Paul and Barnabas into the discipleship of the Messiah without first accepting the whole of the Mosaic law, their resentment mounted.

"Suppose it is true," they argued, "that Jew and Greek are alike before God, and that redemption from sin comes through the Messiah, still he is the Messiah of the Jews. It is only fair that the gentile should accept the Jewish law if he is to be a follower of the Jewish Messiah." Some went to Paul and Barnabas and objected strongly to their attitude toward gentiles. Paul answered by telling them his own story, and how he himself had come to know that Jesus was the Messiah and the Saviour of all mankind.

On the following Sabbath, feelings were tense. When Paul mounted the pulpit, a tumult and shouting began that did not stop until he left the synagogue. In order that the community might not be torn by dissension, the elders asked the two apostles to leave their city.

In Iconium the same things happened. There too the gentiles were interested and the Jews angry. Paul's heart was torn for his own people. He understood how they felt, for had not he also rejected the Gospel? But he also knew the joy that came from accepting it, and he could not bear to have his people deprived of that happiness. But he was more and more convinced that his mission was to the gentiles.

In Lystra, Paul and Barnabas cured a lame man. Then, to their consternation, the entire population, led by their priests, came to adore them as gods and to sacrifice to them. Paul and Barnabas used the opportunity to tell of the one true God. But the people, disappointed that the visitors were not gods in human form as they had thought, would not listen.

Soon troublemakers arrived in Lystra from Antioch and Iconium, and the fickle populace were induced to stone Paul. His enemies left him for dead at the place of stoning. Paul's bruised body seemed lifeless at first to the believers who clustered about him. But, to their amazement and joy, he stirred and then was able to rise. In his suffering he remembered how he had had a part in the stoning of Stephen years ago. Joy in the assurance of God's forgiveness that had come to him through Jesus flooded his spirit. New strength came to him, and with Barnabas he went on to the next city. Everywhere the two left behind them groups of believers, banded together to help establish each other in their faith. Changes in character, joyful spirits, and a new willingness to live in harmony with all others showed that the Spirit of God had indeed come to them.

On the way back to Antioch in Syria, their home base, Paul and Barnabas risked going into all the towns they had visited before. They met with groups of the baptized Christians, organizing them under elders and strengthening them in their faith. Then, since those who had accepted Christ as their Saviour felt commissioned to become missionaries and to tell others about him, they advised them in their missionary work.

Great was the joy in Antioch when Paul and Barnabas reported the success of their journey, particularly when it was learned that so many gentiles had accepted baptism in the name of Jesus. However, a controversy had arisen in Antioch, centering in that very question. Should gentiles who desired to become Christians first accept the faith of the Jews and the law of Moses? The church at Antioch was divided in its answer. Paul and Barnabas traveled to Jerusalem to discuss the matter with Peter, and with James, the brother of Jesus, who had become leader in the Jerusalem church. They took with them Titus, a young gentile Christian, whose genuine faith none could question. Titus was proof to the Christians in Jerusalem that gentiles could share their faith without observing all the Jewish laws. The apostles remembered how years before Peter had been led to baptize the Roman centurion Cornelius. "Go ahead," said Peter and James and the others, to Paul and Barnabas. "It is right that you shall baptize the gentiles without asking adherence to the law of Moses. One thing only do we ask: see that the poor are looked after."

Not all Christians accepted this decision. Some of the Jewish believers would not eat with gentile Christians, fearing they would be lawbreakers if they did so. Paul insisted that this was a denial of the fellowship that believers had in Christ. "It is much more important," he said, "that Christ's love dwell in us than that we observe the ancient laws concerning food." Many Jewish Christians, particularly in Jerusalem, believed they must abide by the laws of their people. They continued to observe all the laws of Judaism, merely adding to them new ways that they had learned in Christ.

After a time Paul went on another missionary journey, accompanied this time by Silas. He was more certain than ever before that, through Jesus, God had made it clear that there is no distinction between Jew and Greek, between slave and free, between male and female—that all are equally important.

Paul and Silas went into Asia Minor through the Cilician Gates, a pass in the Taurus Mountains. They traveled through Paul's home province of Cilicia and then visited the churches established in Galatia. From there they went westward, not knowing just where God wanted them to go next, but feeling sure that he would guide them. The whole world must hear of salvation in Jesus, and there was no time to lose, for Paul believed that Jesus would come again to judge all people. He wanted everyone to know the same joy that he had found as a disciple of Jesus.

At last Paul and Silas came to Troas, on the Aegean Sea. Just a short distance across the waters lay the storied land of Greece and beyond lay Italy and Rome. They prayed earnestly that God would show them what to do. Behind them was Asia, with its many, many cities and countless people to whom they might bring the Gospel; before them was Europe, strange and unknown to them. Where must they go? They wanted to do God's will above all else. That night in a dream there appeared to Paul a man in Macedonian garb who begged, "Come over into Macedonia, and help us." Paul took the dream as a sign from God, and, with Silas and a young disciple, Timothy, who had joined them, he crossed the sea into Europe and arrived at the city of Philippi.

As usual, Paul looked for a synagogue in which to begin his work but he found none, although the city was large. It was not a commercial city, therefore there were few Jews in it. He heard, however, of a group of Jews and their gentile friends who worshiped in a prayer place, a simple enclosure by the water-side where they could easily perform the washings their law demanded, and there he proclaimed his message.

Lydia, a seller of purple, was one of the first of the people of Philippi to become a Christian, and she invited Paul and his companions to make their home in her household. So it was that her house became the first Christian church in Philippi. One day as Paul and his friends were on their way from Lydia's home to the place of prayer, a young half-crazed slave girl, trained in sooth-saying (who made much money for her owners by telling fortunes), called out, "These men are servants of the Most High God; they are the ones who know the way to salvation!" Over and over again she did this, until Paul spoke to her and in the name of Jesus healed her mind and spirit. Because she told no more fortunes after that, her owners were so angered that they had Paul and Silas arrested and brought before the magistrates of the city, charged with sedition. "These men are Jews," they shouted, "and they are teaching customs unlawful for Romans." Under the Roman law, the Jews had certain privileges, but they were not permitted to influence others to accept their faith. Without further trial, the magistrates had Paul and Silas lashed with thongs and cast into prison.

As they lay in prison, Paul and Silas remembered Jesus' saying that following him meant bearing the cross and they began to sing hymns of praise, thanking God that they might suffer in their Master's cause. The jailer heard them and was amazed. That night an earthquake wrecked the prison and left the way open for the prisoners to escape. The jailer, being responsible with his own life for the prisoners, was on the point of committing suicide, when Paul called to him: "Do yourself no harm. We are all here!" Then the jailer's amazement and fright changed to faith. Never had he seen men act like this. He began to question them about the God they worshiped. He asked them to come to his home, where he washed their wounds and brought all his household to be baptized with him into the Christian faith.

Meantime, the magistrates, learning that Paul and Silas were Roman citizens, were distressed that they had treated Romans unjustly and given punishment illegally. They sent word that Paul and Silas might depart quietly from the city, but Paul insisted, "If our punishment was public, so shall our release be public also!" Then the magistrates themselves came and begged them to leave the city.

As a result of the visit of Paul and Silas a thriving church thus began in Philippi. Lydia and the jailer and his family were members of it, and its influence spread into all the surrounding country. Paul left the city, looking forward to later visits to this church he so dearly loved.

Paul and his companions stopped at Thessalonica and several neighboring cities, all of which had large Jewish populations. They made converts in each place. Opposition was so strong in these cities, however, that Paul was forced to leave. Friends accompanied him to Athens, while Silas and Timothy remained behind to establish the new disciples in their faith.

As Paul traveled, he was heavy of heart. Were his own people always to be those who opposed his mission? Was there nothing he could do to help them see the wisdom and the power of God in the crucifixion of the Messiah which they thought a scandal? Would they never understand that merely by keeping the law there was no salvation for any man? The lawless lives he saw in all these pagan cities made him realize what he had never forgotten, how greatly Christians were indebted for all that Israel had suffered and learned through the ages. To them had been given the law and to them had come the prophets declaring the will of God; yet now they were not willing to receive the Messiah in whom God's purpose was fully known. How long would they continue to reject him? The gentile Christians were a branch grafted on the old root of the people of God, and they must never despise the root, although they were becoming the tree. But surely, Paul comforted himself, surely God still loved Israel more than any man could think. "My people are in God's hands," he said to himself, "and one day their blindness will be taken away."

In Athens, city of culture and learning, Paul's heart was saddened to see altars upon altars along the avenues and in the parks—altars to all the gods of the Greeks and Romans. One altar he found inscribed, "To the unknown God." At the market place he spoke to a congregation of philosophers, trying with all the worldly wisdom he could command to explain to them the one God of all the world. But he had no success. His word did not take fire. There were a few who believed, but only a few. Paul did not stay long in Athens. He was eager to leave behind him a city where men were so sure of their own wisdom that they would not try to understand his Gospel.

As Paul went down the road to Corinth, he began to ask himself whether he had made a mistake in trying to speak too wisely to the philosophers of Athens. Perhaps he should have told them more simply the story of Jesus' life and death and resurrection. In Corinth he would make no such mistake. He would declare to them plainly Christ and him crucified.

VII. *"We are ambassadors for Christ . . . : we pray you . . . , be . . . reconciled to God"*

A NEW people of God had come into being out of the remnant of the old. Beyond the story of Paul's labors the Bible tells us little about the spread of Christianity. It is silent about the work of the Twelve after some early stories about Peter and John and the brief report that James, John's brother, was martyred by Herod. Tradition says that Peter was active in Rome. There is also mention of missionary work in provinces other than those visited by Paul, but no report of what was accomplished. How Christianity spread in the Roman Empire under the inspired leadership of the Apostle Paul, and how the new people of God became established, is the last part of the story the Bible tells.

CORINTH was a city that had long interested Paul. He had heard many things concerning it. It had been rebuilt on old ruins at the crossroads of East and West. It was a city with a population that came from here, there, and everywhere, worshiping many gods or none at all; it was known for its worldliness and wickedness.

When Paul arrived in Corinth, to his joy he found a Christian man and his wife, named Aquila and Priscilla, already living there. They had come from Rome and were established in Corinth as weavers of tent cloth. Through their help, Paul at once began work as a weaver. He could make his living at the loom and no one could say then that he was preaching in order to earn money. As Paul wove, he planned and prayed. He felt that God had led him here. How was he to reach the Corinthians' hearts?

"Shall I first tell them, who think there are many gods, about the one true God, holy and righteous?" Paul asked himself. "Shall I tell them first of all about a just and honest way of life before the righteous God, who judges all our actions? What will make them listen?" Then his thoughts went back to the decision he had made on the road from Athens. He would begin with the story that was always at the heart of his message: "I know nothing except Jesus Christ crucified."

In the synagogue on the Sabbath Day, Paul had his chance to speak, and from the moment he began he pleaded with the Jews to see in Jesus their long-promised Saviour. The cross, he declared to them, was a sign of God's love. It was God's care for men and his desire to draw them into fellowship with him that made him willing that the Messiah should suffer for their sakes. But God had also raised him from the dead. Now, none could doubt that God himself had sent him and had raised him to reign on high, whence he would come again to judge all people. Through faith in Jesus, all men now could be reconciled to God and could begin to live a new life in him.

The Corinthians, hungering for knowledge of the truth and for guidance in their lives, listened with deep interest. As Paul told them of Jesus the Messiah and the new life through the Spirit of God that comes to those who live by faith in Jesus, many responded. Life in Christ is a new life, completely different from the old life without him, Paul explained to them. "One must die to sin," was a phrase he loved to use, "to live in Christ, obeying God, loving one's fellow men in the power of the Spirit of God."

While Paul threw the shuttle of his loom back and forth, he planned how not only the city of Corinth, but the whole province of Achaia, of which it was a part, might hear the Gospel. He thought about his converts and decided which of them might be trained as missionaries and sent out to preach. At certain times during the week, as well as on the Lord's Day, he spoke to the growing Christian congregation, which consisted largely of gentiles but was led by Crispus, former head of the synagogue. Gladdened by the arrival of Silas and Timothy, who brought encouraging reports of the faithful converts in Thessalonica and the neighboring region, Paul set them to work ministering to the people of Corinth.

The three companions had much to do. As the gentiles at Corinth had not been trained in life according to moral law, they had to be helped to understand that honesty in business, faithfulness in marriage, and the overcoming of drunkenness and gluttony and loose living are a necessary part of Christian discipleship. "We are the body of Christ," Paul taught them; "we are temples of the Holy Spirit which is within us." They learned to know one of his favorite sayings: "Christ bought us for fellowship with God at a very great price, even his life, therefore we must live for the glory of God."

Angered by the great success of the apostles in Corinth, the Jews brought Paul before the Roman procurator Gallio, charging him with teaching a religion not authorized by Rome (for Judaism alone had a special license to observe rites not in harmony with Roman requirements). Gallio was not interested and sent the accusers away, releasing Paul. However, Paul realized that he might profitably leave the work in Corinth in other hands. The Church in the city was well established and Christian congregations were organized all over the province of Achaia. With his companions he journeyed east, eager to see those he liked to call his children, who through his message had become Christians, and to strengthen the churches he had founded during previous journeys.

"The great province of Asia must next come to know the Gospel," Paul decided, and when he went westward again, he settled in Ephesus, capital of that province. Ephesus was a commercial city on the main road from Rome to the East, made famous by a magnificent temple, of exquisite beauty, dedicated to the goddess Artemis, sometimes called Diana. Aquila and Priscilla were there before him, the two friends whose devotion to Jesus made them missionaries wherever they went. "How I thank God for his grace in giving me such friends as you!" Paul exclaimed, when again they insisted that he share their home. Again he worked at the loom, as they did, for a living. In the school of Tyrannus, a public hall used as a lecture room, Paul gathered a congregation. His first hearers were those whom Aquila and Priscilla had prepared for his message.

While Paul was establishing the work in Ephesus, he ministered to his other churches also, for travelers to Ephesus brought him letters and messages from all over Galatia and Asia, Macedonia and Achaia, asking his advice about many matters. He was particularly troubled by reports from Corinth of discord among the members. Some disciples had not been faithful, and division in the church was threatened. Different factions were claiming to be followers of different teachers, of Paul, of Peter, or of a new teacher, Apollos. Some Corinthians wrote asking Paul's advice about the use of sacrificial meat. The question arose because most of the meat for sale in Corinth had been presented before idols previous to being put on the market. "Since idols have no meaning anyway, what difference does it make whether or not our meat has had any connection with idol worship? But some of the Christians are outraged," the letter said, "because others of us eat such meat."

While Paul worked at his loom, he meditated and prayed and then wrote to the Corinthians, reproving them sharply for uncleanness of life and reminding them again: "You are bought with a price. The body must be a temple of the Holy Spirit." Sacrificial meat in and of itself could not hurt anyone, he told them, but if weaker brothers were offended by the use of such meat, it was better to do without it. As for quarreling over which Christian teacher it is best to follow, is it not well to remember that we are all one body in Christ, who is the head? "Did I die for you?" Paul asked them, "or did Peter? or Apollos? We are all one in Christ; by faith in him we are all children of God, each one serving all with the gifts that are his." Then Paul wrote a song of love, which he sent the Corinthians in his letter. It was a song to tell that Christian love, which has no place for pride or envy or vainglory or selfishness, is the greatest thing in the world, greater even than faith and hope.

Preaching at the school, visiting the sick, meeting with delegations who came from the cities round about, Paul explained at every opportunity the life that is in Christ. Through his ministry and that of his companions Silas and Timothy, and the new disciples whom they trained to be missionaries, many came to live "in Christ" through the power of God's Spirit. The church in Ephesus grew and new churches were established all over the province of Asia.

In the city of Ephesus, devoted to the worship of Diana, many people made a living from the manufacture and the sale of silver images of the great temple. The sale of the little shrines decreased when the numbers of Christ's followers increased. Worried and angered by the decline of his business, Demetrius, chief silversmith, called a meeting of the guild of the shrine makers and associated craftsmen. Filled with indignation, he addressed them, saying: "You know that our wealth in Ephesus comes from the sale of silver shrines. You know that this Jew Paul who has come to our city is influencing not only the Ephesians but also most of the people of our province to believe that there are no gods made with hands. Can you let him go on doing that? There is danger, not only that our trade be ruined, but also that the worship of the great goddess Diana fall into disrepute—our goddess whom people come from afar to worship!"

Someone began to shout, "Great is Diana of the Ephesians!" and the crowd took up the slogan, which was the city's watchword: "Great is Diana of the Ephesians!" Before long a great multitude had gathered, all shouting, not knowing why, "Great is Diana of the Ephesians!" Word went around that the Jews of the city had defamed the goddess. Several of Paul's helpers were found and made prisoners. Paul started to go into the crowd, but some of the chief men of Asia prevailed on him to stay away. The tumult continued, stirring the whole city, until the official representative of Rome appeared. He quieted the multitude, cajoling them with flattery: "Why proclaim what everyone knows?" he asked them. "Everyone is aware of the greatness of this city and of your devotion to your goddess." Then he spoke firmly: "These men are not robbers of temples, as you say, nor blasphemers of your goddess. If any of you have grievances, then appear in lawful assembly and state your case. We are in danger of being called to account for this day's uproar." Quiet was restored as he dismissed the crowd and released the prisoners.

Paul had two dreams that had not yet come true. One was that he might visit Rome, the center of the Empire, where a Christian church had already been established. From there a way might be found, he hoped, that would take him as far west perhaps as Spain. For the present, all he could do about that dream was to write a long letter to the Christians in Rome, telling them his faith and joy as a Christian.

His other dream was that all the Jewish and gentile churches should learn that they were one in Christ. He wanted to teach them to bear one another's burdens and particularly to help the parent church in Jerusalem. The Jerusalem church made it a practice to feed regularly, not only its own poor, but many of the poor of the whole city. "We must help bear that burden," Paul urged upon Christians in other churches, "for our debt is great, not only to the Christians in Jerusalem, but to the whole Jewish people, from whom the Messiah came. He is the Saviour of the whole world, not just the Messiah of the Jews, but it was to the Jews that God saw fit to send him first."

Representatives of the various churches, including the physician Luke, who had been preaching in Philippi, met Paul at Troas. Bearing offerings that had been made by the churches, they set out together for Jerusalem. Paul knew that he was taking his life in his hands, as did his companions. They had all seen the enmity of the Jews in the cities where Paul had preached. In Jerusalem it would be far worse. But it was useless to try to dissuade him from going with them.

Jerusalem was a very restless place. Poverty was even greater than it had been in Jesus' day. The Roman government was more oppressive than before. The high priest and his party were so unfaithful to the people that no one felt any confidence in them. Therefore the influence of the Zealots had grown and often there was violence and tumult.

The people's zeal for the law and for everything that was distinctively Jewish was greater than ever. Easily aroused by any difference of opinion concerning their traditions, they had communicated this uneasiness to the Jews afar and it had been one of the reasons for the quick resentment of Galatians and Macedonians against Paul's teaching. Reports had also come to Jerusalem from the provinces concerning Paul's activities in city after city. These reports had increased the fear for the future of Judaism if the Christian movement continued to grow. Year after year word had come to Jerusalem that all over the Empire Paul's preaching was undermining the faith of the fathers.

Paul and his delegation arrived in Jerusalem just in time for the feast of Pentecost. There were present for the celebration Jews from many merchant cities who knew Paul as the one who had spread the Christian faith throughout their provinces. They recognized some of their fellow citizens among Paul's companions. "Will he make a stir in Jerusalem too?" they asked each other resentfully. When Paul went to worship in the Temple, a false rumor was spread that he had taken gentile companions across the barrier beyond which non-Jews were forbidden to pass. Immediately a riot started. There were desperate men in the mob, and Paul would have been carried away to be stoned for blasphemy had not a Roman official rescued him and taken him to the fortress near the Temple. Granted permission to speak to the mob from the steps of its tower, he began: "My brothers and my fathers! Listen to my defense!" "Hark, he speaks Aramaic!" they said and listened for a time while he told the story of his strict obedience to the law as a Pharisee, his persecution of the Christians, how Jesus himself appeared to him and called him to his service, how he had desired to preach to the people of Jerusalem but they had not trusted him; then the Lord had said, "I will send you to the gentiles." Paul wanted them to know that he was not by any means against his fellow Jews, but everywhere had sought their friendship that the joy which was his in Jesus might be theirs. When he mentioned the gentiles, he was interrupted by loud cries: "Away with that fellow! He deserves to die!" as some threw off their outer garments in preparation for stoning him. Paul was returned to the tower. Later a plot against his life was discovered, and he was taken under guard to Caesarea to be under the protection of the Roman governor there.

Paul sent a reassuring message to the men who had journeyed with him to Jerusalem: "Do not fear for me, for the Lord stood beside me in the night, saying, 'As you testified for me in Jerusalem, so you shall also be my witness in Rome!' "

Luke stayed in the east, following Paul to Caesarea lest he might need a friend there, and using his time to write down the accounts of the stories about Jesus which he had gathered while visiting with James, the brother of Jesus, and the other believers in Jerusalem.

Although nothing could be proved against Paul by those who demanded his death, the corrupt governor was eager to appease his accusers, and kept him in prison for several years. A new governor proposed to return him to Jerusalem for judgment, but Paul made use of his Roman citizenship, saying: "I have done no wrong. I appeal to Caesar!" Such appeal for justice made it the governor's duty to see that the prisoner was conveyed to Rome for trial. Festus, the governor, was embarrassed. "What message can I send the emperor," he wanted to know, "when I can find no legal charges against the prisoner?"

"Perhaps Agrippa can help," he thought. King Agrippa and his sister Bernice had come on a state visit from their territory in northern Palestine. Festus told them of his far-traveled visitor, who even in chains was making many converts to the Christian faith, and whom, it appeared, he must send to Rome guiltless of any crime. Agrippa said, "I should like to hear the man myself!" "You shall hear him tomorrow!" Festus agreed.

The next day, the governor and his guests sat in state, surrounded by their court, when Paul was led before them. Festus said, "I have brought this prisoner before you, King Agrippa, that as the result of your cross-examination I may have something to write the emperor in Rome concerning him, for it seems absurd to me to send a prisoner against whom I have no charges." King Agrippa said, "You are permitted to speak for yourself, Paul!" Putting forth his hand in his accustomed way, although now there were chains about his wrist, Paul began, "I think myself happy, King Agrippa, that I may make my defense before you to-day." Then with passion and ardor he made a defense, not so much of himself as of the Gospel he preached. He told how he had been brought up to share with his people the faith in God's prom-ise of salvation. He recounted how at first he had not believed Jesus of Nazareth to be the fulfillment of that promise. He had even put followers of Jesus into prison and agreed to their execu-tion. But one day, on the way to Damascus, Jesus himself appeared to him in a great light and commissioned him to witness for him in lands afar.

Paul's story moved his hearers deeply as he testified, "I have not been disobedient to the heavenly vision." He told the story of Jesus' crucifixion and resurrection as he had been proclaiming it near and far. "Through faith in him," he said, "those who be-fore lived under the rule of darkness have come to live in light, in the Kingdom of God."

"It is for this testimony that my people desire my death," Paul said. "Why should it be thought incredible that God should send such a message of light to my people and to all people? You must know of it, King Agrippa, for it has not happened in a corner!" Agrippa said, "Almost you persuade me to be a Christian!" Paul answered, "I would to God that not only you but all who hear me today would be what I am—except for these chains!"

Hearing the impassioned appeal of Paul, Luke remembered the words of Jesus that had been told him by disciples in Jeru-salem: "When they take you before magistrates, do not fear, the Holy Spirit will teach you what you shall say."

Agrippa and Festus and those with them went aside to discuss what Paul had said, as well as the testimony of previous hearings. "He has done nothing to deserve death or imprisonment," was their decision. Agrippa said to Festus, "He might have been re-leased if he had not appealed to Caesar."

With a number of other prisoners, and accompanied by his friend Luke, Paul was put on a ship sailing for Rome. The cen-turion Julius was responsible for his welfare. Off the island of Crete the ship was caught in a furious storm. For a day and a night the ship was adrift, tossed violently by wind and wave. On the third day of the hurricane, all except Paul gave up hope. He said to the others: "Have courage, for the angel of God stood by me last night and said, 'Have no fear, Paul, you must be brought before Caesar, and God has given you the lives of all who are on board this ship.' Therefore be cheerful, for I believe it will happen as I was told."

On the fourteenth day of the storm, at midnight, the sailors believed they were nearing land, so, to avoid being driven on rocks, they put out four anchors and waited for the dawn. The sleepless, hungry, and discouraged company looked to Paul as their leader. As day dawned, Paul begged the officers and passengers to take food. "It will make you feel much better. Not a hair from the head of any of you shall be lost." Then he said thanks and began to eat. Seeing his good cheer, the rest also ate. With daylight they came to a beach that promised a safe landing, but the bow of the boat stuck fast and the stern broke away, lashed by the violent waves. The soldiers thought the prisoners ought to be killed, but as Julius wanted Paul saved, he ordered that any who could should swim to shore. When the roll was called, all were safe.

A cold rain was falling, but some of the inhabitants of the island who had seen the shipwreck had hastened to build a fire for the rescued. As Paul gathered up some wood for the fire, a viper wriggled out of it and fastened upon his hand. Assuming that the snake was poisonous, some of the onlookers exclaimed, "That man must be a murderer who cannot escape justice although he has just escaped the sea!" Paul calmly threw the snake into the fire, and when no harm came to him, the same people said, "He must be a god!" The inhabitants of the island, which turned out to be Malta, housed the rescued until a ship was found to take them to Rome. Meantime, by faith and the power of the Spirit of God, Paul cured many on the island who were suffering from various illnesses.

The ship landed at Puteoli, in Italy, some distance from Rome. Word reached Christians in Rome of Paul's arrival and they came to meet him. Paul said, "Thanks be to God for his grace in sending you to me," and was greatly cheered.

Due to the respect he had earned on the voyage and the favorable report Festus had sent the emperor, Paul was treated generously. He had freedom to live in his own rented house. Although always attended by a soldier, he was unhindered in his missionary work. Luke stayed in Rome to be near him, and Mark, who had been a co-worker in earlier days, again assisted Paul in whatever way he could. To Paul's joy, Christians who had moved to Rome from the provinces and travelers who were members of churches he had founded, came to visit their "father in Christ." Paul rejoiced also to make friends among the many Roman Christians. He planned with them the spread of the Church to the West, possibly as far as Spain. He discussed with them many of the matters concerning which he had written his long letter to them. Paul invited non-Christian Jews to visit him, for always his love for his own people caused him to wish for them the joy he had in fellowship with God in Christ. He told them of his faith in Jesus as Messiah, how he himself had seen "the glory of God in the face of Jesus Christ," and some of them believed.

One day, there came to him a slave who had run away to Rome, having stolen money from his Christian owner, whom Paul knew at Colossae. Under Paul's influence, this slave, Onesimus (a name meaning "useful"), became a Christian. And then the question was, Must Onesimus give up his freedom and return to his owner? Paul said yes, he must, but that his Christian owner must receive him as a brother.

He sent Onesimus back to Philemon with a letter saying: "I want to appeal to you on behalf of my spiritual son. Onesimus, true to his name, has become very useful to you and to me, although in the past he was anything but useful to you. Perhaps you were parted for a while so that you might have him back as more than a slave—indeed as a dear brother. If you are concerned about the money he stole from you, put the debt down to my account! I will repay it! I know that you will do even more than I tell you." Paul did not need to say to Philemon, "In Christ there is neither slave nor free, as there is neither Jew nor Greek," for his friend knew that was what the whole letter was saying: "We are all one in Christ Jesus."

Paul wrote also to his friends in Philippi. He told them that his imprisonment was not an obstacle to the spreading of the Gospel, but rather a help. Being a prisoner had opened up new fields of service for Christ, including even the household of the emperor. "I believe that I shall be released," he told them, "but what matters is that Christ shall be known through me. It is not important whether I live or die. It is a privilege to suffer for his sake." He urged the Philippians to have joy in fellowship with the Lord: "Rejoice in the Lord always, and again I say, rejoice!"

Evil times came upon the Christians in the city of Rome. Because their way of life and worship was different from any known before, many Romans looked upon them with suspicion and enmity. When a great fire made many Romans homeless, the hated emperor Nero, who was known to have plans for rebuilding the city, was accused of having set the fire deliberately. To deflect the attention of the enraged citizens from himself, Nero accused the sect of Christians of guilt, and they were cruelly persecuted. Among the many who gave up their lives for their faith during these days was Paul.

The death of their "father in Christ" was the cause of great mourning among the Christians, but also a source of new courage, for they knew that the apostle for whom no hardship had been too great that Christ might be made known had been glad to die for the Gospel's sake. They were happy for him, who had written his friends but recently: "Both life and death mean Christ to me. It would be hard for me to choose. Staying here means fruitful work and serving you. But my strong desire is to go and be with Christ."

The churches exchanged with each other the letters Paul had written them, and made extra copies of them, until each church had for its guidance a collection of his words of advice and counsel and discipline and inspiration. The Christians read them and meditated upon them, and so the ministry of Paul continued. God had used Paul as his chief instrument in establishing a new people for himself. Its Head was Christ and it included all persons everywhere who obeyed God's will. As Paul had written in his letter to the Romans, "As many as are led of the Spirit of God, they are the children of God."

VIII. *"Nor height, nor depth, nor any other creature, shall be able to separate us from the love of God . . . in Christ Jesus"*

AT THE close of the century in which Jesus was born, a Christian leader wrote: "I suppose if everything that Jesus did were written down, and all that he accomplished in God's plan for mankind, the world would not contain the books that would be written."

Before our Bible story is complete, there remains to be told the story of the books which, with Paul's letters and some letters written by other leaders, came to be the New Testament. When we know how these books were written, we shall understand something of the life of the early Christians after the death of their first leaders, and what God's plan for salvation as fulfilled in Jesus meant to them.

WHAT shall we do when all who knew the Lord Jesus have died?" Christians were asking one another. "Who will tell us what he said and did? How will new Christians hear the story of the cross and the resurrection?" Some parents asked, "How will our children's children be taught the story when we are no longer alive to tell them what we heard from those who were with him?"

John Mark in Rome was among those who asked these questions, and he knew it was important that something be done. Many of the aged among his Christian friends and acquaintances had died; then Nero's persecution had robbed the Christian fellowship of still more of its leaders. Mark resolved: "I must finish now what I have begun. I must set down in writing the Gospel the apostles have been preaching."

Mark, a relative of Paul's friend Barnabas, had been a youth in Palestine in Jesus' day. In the early days of the Church, his mother's house had been a gathering place for the Christians, and there Mark had listened often when the disciples told the story of Jesus' life and death and resurrection. Peter was a frequent visitor in his home; indeed, it was there he had gone after an imprisonment in the early days of his preaching. Then Mark had been associated with Peter in his work and had heard over and over the story of Jesus as Peter told it from his own experience. Mark had also helped Paul and Barnabas in their early missionary work. During Paul's imprisonment in Rome, Mark again heard the story as Paul told it.

Mark had begun some time before to collect short accounts of Jesus' life that had been written down in some of the churches for the training of the new disciples. Soon after Paul's death, when it became clear to him that he must record what the apostles had been preaching, he sat down to write a connected story that he called "the gospel of Jesus Christ." It was a good name, for his story was the message that the apostles, wherever they went, had been proclaiming as the Gospel, the good news, of Jesus Christ.

While Mark was writing his Gospel, the sorrows of the persecution in which Paul lost his life lay heavy on the Christians. Mark said: "I must help my friends to see how strong was the power of God in Jesus. They must know that through him all evil can be conquered." The Christians in Rome took heart when they read Mark's Gospel, for it reminded them that the power of God which was in Christ had come upon the disciples too. God would do great works through them, as he had done through

Christ, and he would give to each of them the strength he needed to bear his own cross.

Visitors in Rome made copies of Mark's Gospel for use in their home churches. These manuscripts were copied again for use in surrounding regions. Before long, Mark's Gospel was used far and wide in the Church.

In Jerusalem and Antioch and other Eastern churches, the people were happy to have Mark's story, but they were not completely satisfied. It was a very short book, and many of them knew stories and sayings that were not included. There were many members in these churches who had known the first disciples. Indeed, some were still living who had themselves known Jesus. They wanted a more complete story. And they liked having more of Jesus' teachings included than were found in Mark's Gospel.

Some collections of Jesus' teachings, short sayings, and also parables, were being used in the churches to guide the Christian fellowship. By means of them the children and the new members were taught how to live as followers of Jesus. One of these collections—the largest one—perhaps originally made by the disciple Matthew, was known as "Matthew's Oracles."

Among the Eastern Christians, probably in Antioch, there was a devout and gifted man who knew what he must do to make the more complete record his fellow Christians were desiring. He took Mark's Gospel and Matthew's Oracles, as well as other collections of stories and sayings that were known in Jerusalem and Antioch. Then he wove together all this material into one story.

While this writer planned and wrote, he had an important purpose constantly in mind. He wanted not only to compose a more complete story, but also to help both Jewish and gentile Christians to understand the connection of the Gospel of Jesus with all that God had done for his people in the past. It seemed important to him, who was himself a Jewish Christian, for all members of the Christian Church to understand that Jesus had not come unexpectedly, but that his coming had been prepared for by God in all the history of the Jewish people. He wanted Christians to know that Jesus' coming was part of a great plan that God had for all the world, in which the people of Israel had been very important. Christians must be aware of the fact, he believed, that the law which his people had been taught to revere and to obey was a schooling for the kind of obedience that comes from the love of God as they learned it in Jesus. So this Christian man wrote the book that came to be known as "The Gospel According to Matthew," in which he showed how God prepared the way for the salvation of mankind through Israel.

Matthew's Gospel was read far and wide, and helped to unite the Church. The Church needed to remember that it must always be one, for there were people who would have been happy to see it divided and destroyed. Titus, who later became emperor in Rome, thought that, if there were no church in Jerusalem, all the other Christian churches throughout the world would soon die. Therefore, when he sent his armies against the city of Jerusalem in A.D. 70, he hoped to strike a deathblow at the very heart of the Christian Church.

The Romans had other reasons for becoming impatient and angry with Jerusalem. Some years before, the emperor Caligula had endeavored to set up his image in the Temple of Jerusalem. The Jews had resisted to the utmost. Fortunately the emperor died before the matter came to an issue. However, the old disaffection against Rome had increased greatly at that time and had grown steadily since then. One rebellion succeeded another, until finally the emperor Titus sent his armies to take Jerusalem, and after a harassing siege destroyed it. Not one stone remained upon the other, as Jesus had foretold. The Christians of Jerusalem fled to Pella. Since the days of Peter and James they had remained loyal to the traditions of Judaism, obeying the law of Moses, so that their ways were different from those of the gentile churches. When the Romans rebuilt Jerusalem, they named it "Aelia Capitolina," and for a time no Jews were permitted to enter it. The days of the parent church in Jerusalem were over.

Christians everywhere knew by this time that they were a new people of God, not dependent upon any temple or city for their unity. They thought of themselves, wherever they might be, as members of one "body of Christ." When they read Matthew's Gospel, Jewish and gentile Christians alike claimed it as their own. The gentile Christians said: "The scriptures of the Jews, the Old Testament, belong to us also. What God said to Israel through the prophets he said for us all. What the Israelites suffered to become God's people, they suffered for us all in preparation for the coming of Him whom God sent to be the Redeemer of the world."

As there came to be more and more gentile churches in which the members knew little or nothing of the Jewish people and their history, the need was felt for a Gospel that would be written specially for them. Luke, the physician friend and companion of Paul, himself a gentile Christian, was concerned about these gentile Christians. He also knew some thoughtful Greek-speaking pagans whom he wanted to interest in the Christian faith. The Gospel of Mark was short, written in not very good Greek, and, like Matthew's Gospel, it took for granted many things that were familiar to Jews but not to gentiles. Luke himself understood well the Jewish expectation of the Messiah, as did the other gentile Christians whom Paul had taught, but he said: "The Messiah who came to the Jews is the Saviour of all the world. I will write a Gospel that will help my friend Theophilus, who is not yet a Christian, to see what this means. My book will show gentile Christians that the Messiah of the Jews is their Saviour and the Saviour of all mankind."

When Luke was with Paul in Jerusalem and in Caesarea, he had gathered all the stories about Jesus that he could find. Many that he cherished were not included in the other Gospels. He knew that he must make available to all Christians the beautiful stories of Jesus' infancy and childhood that were current in the Church but no one else had recorded: how when he was born in Bethlehem an angel chorus sang in celebration, "Glory to God in the highest," and how shepherds who had been watching their flocks by night hastened to adore the child. No one else had told the story Luke had learned of the visit of the twelve-year-old boy Jesus to the Temple in Jerusalem, where he had listened to the teachers of the law and asked them questions. Luke also knew stories of Jesus' prayer life, told him by people who had been close to the Master, which he knew he must tell. Luke was particularly fond of stories that showed how Jesus' love extended to all people; how, repeatedly, Samaritans, despised of the Jews, had been singled out for praise by him, and how, at the end of his mission, he commanded his disciples to preach the Gospel to all nations.

So Luke began to write. He addressed his Gospel to his friend Theophilus, who to his mind represented the many pagans who might become Christians. Luke told of Jesus as the one who came as the glory of the people Israel, but also as a "light to lighten the gentiles." He did not tell much about Jesus' attitude toward the law, but he told a great deal about his teaching concerning repentance and forgiveness. He wrote down a story Jesus had told about a publican who prayed humbly, "God be merciful to me a sinner," and whose prayer pleased God, rather than the Pharisee's, who said proudly to God, "I thank thee that I am not like so many other people." Luke told also the story of the Prodigal Son, whose father forgave him when he returned home and asked to be accepted as a servant, and the stories of the Lost Sheep and the Lost Coin—parables that showed Jesus' desire to reach and to help people who had made failures of their lives. It gave Luke great joy too that he could report certain words Jesus spoke when he was hanging on the cross that had not been set down before. One of these was Jesus' prayer for his enemies: "Father, forgive them; for they know not what they do."

When Luke had written his Gospel, he began a second book, the story of the beginnings of the Church in Jerusalem, and of the spread of the Church westward to Rome. In writing this story he used diaries that he had kept when he was with Paul, as well as accounts of other helpers of the apostles, and Paul's own story of his conversion and his work. This book, which became known as "The Acts of the Apostles," showed how through faith in Jesus a new people of God had come into being. It told how knowledge of Jesus had transformed the lives of his disciples so that no suffering for his name was too great, that indeed, they gloried in the fact that they were considered worthy to suffer for the sake of the Gospel.

Among the Christians who, like Paul, could not imagine life without Christ was one named John, who said, "Someone must tell the story of Jesus so that people will know the life of fellowship with God which he made possible!" So this Christian, who may have been John the Elder, a leader in the Western Church, wrote a fourth Gospel, the last in our Bible. He began, not with the story of Jesus' birth or with his baptism, as the others had done, but with God the Creator. John started by saying: "God wanted man to have fellowship with him, so he clothed his will and his thought in human form. God came and dwelt among men in the person of Jesus." Then John went on to tell the story of Jesus' life, making clear that Jesus showed man what God is like and that he helped men become children of God, God's true sons, through repentance for their sins and through faith in God's power and mercy. To the people waiting for Jesus' return, John's Gospel said: "He does not need to return to be with us. He has come to us through the Spirit of God whom he sent to dwell in us." It was a wonderful book that John wrote out of his knowledge of Jesus' life on earth and out of his own prayer and meditation upon the life of fellowship with God into which Jesus had brought him.

During the latter part of the first century many Christians paid with their lives for their Christian faith. "Why can you not worship your god and the emperor too?" the Romans asked, and could not understand when the Christians preferred to die rather than burn incense before the image of the emperor. Emperor worship had been made increasingly important in the Empire, and Christians, since they would not take part in it, were treated as outlaws. Even kindhearted Romans thought this was as it should be, and there were hardhearted governors and magistrates who made the Christians endure torture and indignity and cruel death.

In these days of suffering, there lived in the province of Asia another Christian leader named John, who was exiled by the Roman authorities to the island of Patmos in the Aegean Sea because of his influence, and as punishment for preaching Christ. It was a lonely island, where criminals were sent to work in the stone quarries. John spent much time in meditation. Often he sat by the sea, watching the sunset while he prayed for seven Christian churches in the province of Asia—the church of Ephesus and six neighboring churches—where lived the Christians he knew best. He knew the strength and the weaknesses of these different churches, and also the trials which their members might be called upon to endure. He remembered that the emperor's name day would be celebrated again, when feeling would run especially high against any who did not join the rest of the population in adulation of the emperor. In this prosperous part of the Empire, the emperor Domitian was revered as "Lord and God," and commemorated with much pomp and ceremony. "Suppose some of our Christians are asked to decide: 'Caesar or Christ!' and in fear of torture and death deny their Lord? Suppose, the emperor's name day safely past, they cannot stand the strain of knowing that any day an informer may report them to be Christians? Suppose they would rather do homage before the emperor's image and deny Christ than be condemned to death as traitors?"

John's own faith was strong and unshakable, and it had been strengthened by knowledge of the many Christians who had suffered gladly for Christ's sake, some who had even gone singing to their death in arenas where wild beasts awaited them. He wanted to help the Christians in the seven churches to be firm and unfaltering too, glad to suffer for the name of Him who had died for them all. And in the meantime he wanted them to live lives worthy of the name of Christ.

So John, who is sometimes called John the Seer, decided to write a letter to the seven churches, in which he would tell them, by way of the visions that had come to him, of the glory of God's government of the world and the victory for righteousness which had come through Christ and would come finally for all the world to know. Also, he would warn them of God's judgment upon their sins. So John wrote, beginning: "John to the seven churches which are in Asia! Grace be to you and peace from him who is and was and is to come." He went on to promise that he would tell them "the revelation of Jesus Christ" which God gave to him. He told the seven churches what things they were doing well and where they were failing, since he could not come in person to guide them. Then he tried to make clear to them how much greater and more wonderful is the unseen world of the spirit than the world we can see. The good in the world is continually beset by evil, John told his readers, but we are never left alone to fight the battle against evil. In one vision after another he pictured how the powers of darkness will be overthrown in one crisis after another, until finally God will create a new heaven and a new earth.

John could hardly find words to tell the glory of the triumph of righteousness that would come in God's own time. In his vision he saw a new Jerusalem coming down from heaven which would have gates of pearl that would never be closed, for people to enter from all the ends of the earth. Nothing unclean would enter the city. Its streets would be of gold and its walls gleaming with emeralds and sapphires and other precious stones. When John wanted to tell the glory of the unseen world, he used all the images of the most beautiful things he had seen to describe it. He could not think of words wonderful enough to describe Christ, ruling at the right hand of God over the new heaven and earth. "The bright and morning star" is one of John's names for him. He tells his readers of a vision of angels blowing trumpets before the throne of God, of great multitudes of the redeemed of earth in white garments who sing songs of victory over evil—songs celebrating salvation—and of God upon his throne, saying, "Behold, I make all things new."

With these visions of John the story that the Bible tells comes to its end. In one glorious picture after another the mercy and the power of God shine forth clearly. We see how, in sending Christ, God found a way to help us have the fellowship with him for which he created us. We see that his mercy and power are great enough to bring to pass a time foretold by the prophet of old, when "the knowledge of God will cover the earth as the waters cover the sea."

SCRIPTURE REFERENCES

SCRIPTURE REFERENCES